FIBERGLASS BOATS

Construction and Maintenance

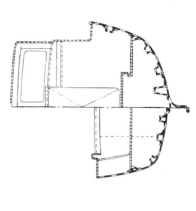

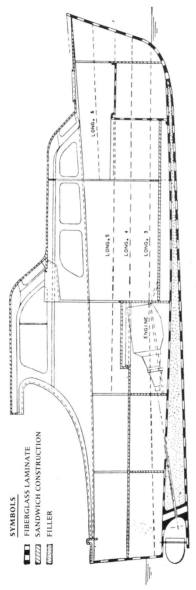

SYMBOLS

■ FIBERGLASS LAMINATE
▨ SANDWICH CONSTRUCTION
▨ FILLER

Some or all of these structural features will be found in a given fiberglass power boat. Fiberglass hull shell is stiffened with longitudinal fiberglass hat sections or girders. The centrally positioned longitudinals may be used to mount the engines. Plywood bulkheads are generally used for transverse stiffening and strength. Deck and house tops employ some type of core material in whole or in part to provide maximum stiffness and light weight. Depending on design, heavy or light weight filler materials are placed in the hollow keel section.

FIBERGLASS BOATS

Construction and Maintenance

By BOUGHTON COBB JR.

FOURTH EDITION

New York

ZIFF-DAVIS PUBLISHING CO.

Fourth Edition

Printed in the United States of America

Library of Congress number 78-58361

ISBN 0-87165-015-0

vi

INTRODUCTION

THIS BOOK represents a collection of articles on fiberglass boat construction developed by the author over a twelve-year period for YACHTING magazine.

The author's special vantage point has been from his employment with a raw-material supplier, Owens Corning Fiberglas, and a long-time hobby interest in pleasure craft. As a result, the material reflects the writer's observations and interest in process and material combined with an appreciation of the practical knowledge we think that a boat owner would like to have.

BOUGHTON COBB, JR.

New York, N.Y.
April, 1973

CONTENTS

CHAPTER 1

Origins of the Industry

FIBERGLASS IS PASSING into its third decade of usage as a boat-building material. The time span is not so long, but great enough to give the material a history of some interest. In recent years, questions of who built the first glass boats, what did they look like, how were they constructed, have been asked. The historical facts are not well documented.

One of the reasons that it is difficult to accept accurate, early information on glass hulls is that the construction concept really evolved into being rather than occurring as an invention at a definite point of time. Modest research shows that many engineers and craftsmen in widely separated parts of the country were working along parallel lines on plastic hulls during the early 1940's. The writer is not well informed on the history of glass reinforced plastic hulls abroad, but there is good reason to believe the United States was first with the concept, certainly so on a production basis.

The idea of combining a fibrous reinforcement with plastic-like materials is not new. Even ancient people understood and applied the principles with organic materials. However, until the modern age of chemistry and synthetics, strength and particularly durability were limited. For a number of reasons, World War II marks a period when materials technology began to expand rapidly. A great deal had to do with acute shortages which stimulated interest in new or substitute materials. But more than this, modern chemistry was beginning to offer a whole new generation of synthetics with markedly superior qualities.

Glass fibers for reinforcing plastics were pretty much in their commercial infancy during the war, although glass in spun wool form was rather well established for insulation purposes. Owens-Corning pioneered the commercial production of glass fiber, having emerged in 1938 as a corporation born of Owens Illinois and Corning Glass.

The most important ingredient, of course, was a suitable resin to bind the glass together and form a durable composite. Many types of resins have been and are currently used in conjunction with glass fiber, but the development of polyester which would cure at room temperature and without pressure was a key contribution which really sent the industry on its way. While completely suitable polyester resins did not appear until after the war, between 1946 and 1947, the true beginnings of the process seemed to have occurred during the war years, largely stimulated by the government. The Navy gave authorization that the use of plastics should be explored for small craft. There were several pioneering companies. Ray Greene, a builder of fiberglass sailboats in Toledo, who has been in the business since its inception, reports that development work in plastic hulls was being carried on by many small inventive groups during the war—including himself. As a naval officer with some background in the early art he had a directive position with the Navy's basic survey and planning.

Developments on the west and east coasts seem to have led most directly to what can be considered the earliest production quantities of glass boats. In southern California a company called Chemold was contracted by the military in 1943-44 to produce molded plastic hulls. Among the designs was the air drop rescue "Dumbo" carried by B-17's. Chemold reportedly employed a cold molding system with an acetate resin. The reinforcement was osnaburg cotton, a type of muslin. When the war ended, the tooling was sold to the neighboring Wizard Boat Co., whom many readers will remember. Wizard developed a line of outboards and was in business up until recent years. The Wizard people employed polyester resin and glass reinforcement in combination with the osnaburg cloth in 1946. The boats were formed over a male mold, a practice they continued for some time even though the rest of the glass boat industry was using cavity molds. The Glasspar Company started in 1947, close on the heels of Wizard. Bill Tritt, founder of Glasspar, now living in Santa Barbara, Cal., reports that he first produced sailboats rather than the outboards which made the company famous. His initial models were a male-molded sandwich of glass between muslin or osnaburg cotton. The polyester resin from American Cyanamid was very hard to handle and, what seems incredible by today's production standards, required a sunlight cure. Catalysts were not properly developed and the ultraviolet rays of the sun were relied upon. Once the hulls were laid up they were wheeled into an outside curing yard. One can suppose that no hulls were built during the California "wet sunshine" season.

On the East Coast process developments had a somewhat different character. Emphasis was placed on rather heavy, complicated tooling systems. This may have been due to the influence of molded plywood techniques which employed pressure bags and heated autoclaves. In addition, it must be recognized that most plastics up to that time were processed under heat and pressure. The Navy believed that a mechanized pressure process of some sort would yield a better structural laminate.

In June, 1946, the Winner Co. in Trenton, N.J., received a Navy contract to develop a fiberglass 28' personnel boat shown in the accompanying photographs. Winner's early development work involved sisal-reinforced polyester and, in fact, they produced quite a few small pleasure craft with this organic reinforcement before switching to glass in 1947. The organic reinforcements like sisal and osnaburg cotton lacked the strength of glass, but more important, they were not resistant enough to water absorption and general deterioration that often occurred after extended immersion. Sisal was employed by a number of plastic boat

The U.S. Navy's first fiberglass boat, a 28' personnel craft produced under a development contract to Winner Mfg., Trenton, N.J., about 1946, one of the earliest fiberglass boats built.

Interior stiffening structure in hull of Navy 28-footer (right) utilizes wooden members in the laminate. Winner runabout (below left) at a 1947 boat show. Hulls were molded with bag pressure in heated metal cavity. A 24' Beetle cruiser (below right) about 1949. While oddly styled by today's standards, hull was ruggedly built and gave good service.

companies of that era. Visually the first sign of failure was distortion of the hull followed by delamination. Obviously, not all the organic reinforced hulls were unsatisfactory. There are still some in operation today. But as glass fiber became available, it was clearly a better choice.

Production of the Navy 28-footers at Winner's continued up until the early '50s. Apparently some are still in service today, one or two in a civilian capacity. The first hulls, in 1947, were produced with a massively heavy and expensive tooling—metal cavity hull and deck molds, with a pressure bag. It was necessary because the particular polyester resin required heat and pressure to cure. The deck mold alone weighed 11 tons—an air lock chamber complete with telephone was designed into the rubber bag so that workmen could crawl inside to make adjustments and smooth out wrinkles. Needless to say, if the industry were bound to this production system today, the molding of glass hulls would be very

Typical early fiberglass runabouts featured wooden decks, seats, rails. This one was produced by Northwest Fiberglass Co., Minn.

Lone Star Boat Co. went all out to provide automotive styling afloat. This was an industry fad which was short-lived.

In 1959 Hatteras introduced the first production line
stock cruiser in fiberglass.

impractical. Winner switched over to a simplified open mold method on
the 28's as soon as the proper resin system became available in 1947.

Winner does appear to have been the first volume producer of glass
hulls, coming out with a small line in the years 1946 and 1947. These
were manufactured with a pressure bag and heated metal cavity mold.
They stayed with this process exclusively for quite a long time. Eventually
Winner gave up their pleasure boat business, but the name continued on
under Winner Boats of Dickson, Tenn.

Certain established boatbuilders in New England were among the
very earliest in the fiberglass boat field. Cape Cod Shipbuilding, Beetle,
The Anchorage, Palmer Scott are well-known companies which made
substantial contributions to the art. As an old-line wooden boat building
company, Cape Cod made a very decisive shift to fiberglass in the years
1948 and 1949. By 1952 only two per cent of their production was in
wood. Les Goodwin, president of Cape Cod, reports that he was initially
unsure about consumer acceptance, but quickly found there was little
resistance. At the outset, Cape Cod selected the open cavity mold
technique for production, employing glass mat as the exclusive reinforcement. Their basic approach has remained unchanged throughout the
years.

Beetle and Palmer Scott, however, started out with rather heavy
tooling techniques recommended to them by raw material suppliers.
Beetle's first hulls in 1948 were molded at the General Electric Company
in Pittsfield, Mass., where General Electric had its polyester resin
development facilities. From what we can determine these dinghy and
small sailboat hulls were formed under bag pressure in heated metal

5

Fortier

Rose

Left—Earliest large fiberglass sailboat, the 42' ketch "Arion," built by The Anchorage in 1950. Rhodes-designed Bounty (right) was popular in wood before the war. Recreated in fiberglass by Coleman in 1956, she started demand for glass auxiliaries.

cavity molds. Newly developed glass fiber mat from Owens-Corning was the principal reinforcement. In a year or two, Beetle had established the simpler room temperature contact process in fiberglass cavity molds at their own plant in New Bedford. For a number of years Beetle's name was synonymous with small fiberglass craft. They heavily advertised the features of fiberglass.

Palmer Scott switched to fiberglass late in the '40s. The yard had been well-known for its fine wooden sailing auxiliaries. In going into fiberglass they chose a mated mold, vacuum injection system which plastics expert Dr. Muscat had developed and had the backing of the Navy. The process had only short-lived and limited popularity with pleasure boat builders, but the Palmer Scott people turned out quite a few navy and pleasure craft before switching to the now conventional contact lay-up system.

The late Bill Dyer of The Anchorage in Warren, R.I., started in fiberglass at about the same time as Cape Cod, 1948-1949. Best known for his yacht tenders and racing dinghies, Bill set a high standard of workmanship for the new industry. Dyer built some of the earliest large glass hulls. The 42' ketch **Arion**, 1950, is still serving well at the Coast Guard Academy, and in 1952 The Anchorage built three 40' Coast Guard patrol boats which are still going strong.

Left—The 30' Atlantic, a classic design from the 1920's, was produced in glass by Cape Cod Shipbuilding during the mid-1950's. Carl Alberg's Triton (right), produced by Pearson, is modestly-priced glass auxiliary which has enjoyed great popularity.

Throughout the early years there was great interest in finding an automated or machine-controlled process which could realize high rates of production and corresponding low costs. Reinforced plastic seemed to have this potential for boat hulls as the principle had been demonstrated on small plastic parts. But the industry did not have the unit volume in any one model. They disliked high capital investment and the lack of tooling and design flexibility. The sentiments are much the same today. It took the courage and initiative of one firm, the Molded Fiberglass Co., to show that heavy tooling could be used efficiently to produce outboard hulls. M.F.G. molded their first matched die hulls around 1956. They are still using the process today on many of their high volume models.

Looking back now at the process development aspects of fiberglass hulls, one can probably say that the boat molders themselves deserve the greatest credit. Contact molding, which has proved to fit the boat industry best, required the resin and glass suppliers to work out many small but critical refinements so that this simple lay-up technique could gain a true production status.

In establishing a new material and construction concept, particularly in a tradition-bound industry, elaborate claims and promotion are probably inevitable. The fiberglass boat industry received much criticism in this regard. General ignorance about the legitimate properties and

7

characteristics of the material probably contributed more to the problem than overstated claims by a relatively few companies. One must remember too that after the war plastic had a stigma attached to it. Producers of fiberglass boats had to battle this negative public opinion. To disprove the idea that glass hulls would shatter and crack, promotion-minded builders carried out a variety of stunts. In the January, 1949 issue of YACHTING there is a description of a Wizard fiberglass hull which somehow survived: (1) a second story drop on to a concrete sidewalk, (2) a beating from a 16-lb. sledge and (3) a barrage of pistol bullets. Such demonstrations must have proved a point, but some literal minded fiberglass boat owners were disappointed when their own craft did not measure up to this durability standard. Exaggerated claims and promotion which created the idea that fiberglass hulls were virtually indestructible and free from maintenance did not rest well with responsible members of the industry. In the mid-1950s legal restraints were imposed on boat advertising claims.

Looking at the earliest advertising copy on fiberglass hulls, it is interesting to note that there is little or no mention of the word fiberglass. The word plastic was carefully veiled and modified. The boatbuilders using the new material needed a single descriptive word which differentiated their product and was promotable. They found it in "fiberglass."

CHAPTER 2

Properties and Principles of Fiberglass Reinforcements

AS OWNERSHIP AND FAMILIARITY with fiberglass boats have grown, seriously interested boatmen have wanted to gain a greater understanding of the materials and construction techniques. One aspect that comes up often concerns the form of glass-fiber reinforcement which may be used in hull construction. Considerable variation in the type of fiberglass reinforcement is found from one builder to another. Naturally, the question is "What is best?"

A precise answer to this question is not possible; but the reasons why the different designs of fiberglass are chosen are interesting and useful.

Some Basic Principles

Reinforcing a plastic with glass fibers is similar to the principle of reinforcing concrete with steel rods. The fiberglass or the steel is the load-carrying member of the combination. The plastic resin or the concrete holds the reinforcing members in position so they can do their job effectively. This analysis is naturally an oversimplification, but it is useful in pointing out the relationships between the glass and the resin.

This basic concept is apparently misunderstood by many who loosely refer to these craft as "plastic boats," "reinforced fiberglass boats," and so on. To be sure, there are some small plastic craft on the market today which are not reinforced with glass fiber, and these are distant cousins to the laminated fiberglass type. However, they do not exhibit the same high specific-strength properties.

The importance of the laminating resin used in the lay-up of fiberglass craft should not be played down. Actually, it was the development of a suitable polyester plastic, in about 1944, which gave birth to this concept of construction. But it is important to point out that the glass fibers themselves are the load-bearing and stabilizing members of the combination. Some verification of this is seen in an examination of the earliest fiberglass boats and molded parts which were made with resin far less advanced than that which we have today. Many of these early prototypes are still performing satisfactorily. While the reinforced areas are chipped, abraded and cracked, the body of the laminate, properly interlaced with glass filament, is in a remarkably sound condition.

9

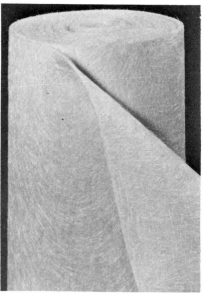

Fiberglass reinforcing filaments generally originate from marbles. Up to 90 miles of filament is provided by each marble.

Fiberglass reinforcing mat is composed of strand laid down in a jackstraw pattern and loosely bonded with a small percentage of chemical binder.

Fiberglass Reinforcements in Boat Construction

An observant person who spends a little time comparing fiberglass boats will note that there are different glass-reinforcing materials used. Often this is visually apparent in the interior areas of the craft where the surface is usually formed without contact with a mold surface. You may logically ask why different materials are used. Is one reinforcement stronger or better than another? The following is directed towards explaining the uses of these materials.

Basic Forms of Reinforcement

There are two basic forms of glass reinforcement used in molded boat construction today—random chopped fiber and woven glass fabric. The chopped-fiber type may be furnished to the builder in the form of a felted matting, or he may chop and disperse the strand into the mold by the use of a fiber-chopper gun (to be discussed later).

There are several types of glass-fiber mats, but the most popular are the chopped-strand type. The cut strands are laid down in a random jackstraw pattern and loosely bonded together with a chemical binder to

Fiberglass filaments are formed into strands, twisted and plied into yarns, then woven into cloth. Fabrics are chemically treated in order that the plastic resin will adhere to the glass. This is a standard "boat cloth" used in the molding and covering of boats.

A heavy, coarse fabric called woven roving. This style is almost three times the weight of the boat cloth shown at left—is used as a primary structural reinforcement in molded boats.

make the product hold together for handling and layup. Mats are supplied in various widths and weights.

Fabrics are woven from continuous glass filament produced on a textile type loom and are supplied in many different weave designs and weights. For boat molding or covering, the plain, square weave is almost universally used because it forms well, allows for rapid impregnation and is relatively economical. These fabrics range in weight from about 6 oz. to 20 oz. per square yard.

Woven roving is actually a fabric of a heavy, coarse nature. Strands are roved together, not twisted as they are in fabric, which makes the material unique and gives it a distinctive look. Woven roving is less expensive than fabric and has good physical properties.

From this it can be seen that there are just two basic types of glass reinforcement used in boat molding—woven materials and cut strand. The specific combinations in a laminate can vary widely because of the different weights of cloth or mat and the sequence in which they are laid up. Fabrics and chopped fiber mattings are used singly or in combination to build up the necessary strength and rigidity in a boat. While either type of reinforcement may be used exclusively for the entire structure, it is more common to find the chopped and woven materials used in combination. Most of the very early fiberglass boats were molded with cloth exclusively, before woven roving and mats were available. Cloth is excessively expensive for thick build-ups, and the coarse, heavy woven roving was subsequently designed to give the properties of fabric at a much more reasonable cost.

Because builders are prone to promote their individual hull designs and construction techniques, the public is led to believe that there must be definite, superior material choices. Perhaps unhappily so for the interested buyer, there is no clear straightforward answer as to which material is best. Each has its advantages and disadvantages. A good builder will know how to get the most out of each material, and by engineering refinements in the boat itself will bring out the best in structural performance. While there are many individual preferences in the use of glass reinforcements between different builders, some commonly accepted principles will be of interest to the technically inclined reader.

Comparative Characteristics of Woven and Chopped Fiberglass

It may be well to point out what factors the builder is considering when he makes his glass-reinforcement selection. The important ones are cost, strength, ease of molding and finished appearance.

Using chopped-fiber mat as a reinforcement, he will have a material cost significantly below fabric, but somewhat higher than the less processed strands which are applied with a chopper gun. Chopped strand does not have the high tensile strength of fabric, but it has other superior features and is fully eligible as a structural reinforcement. Because of its random pattern, mat is a more homogeneous reinforcement than fabric and has a much more uniform strength distribution. It exhibits uniform strengths throughout 360°, whereas fabrics show their high values only in the direction of the lay of the strands; i.e., 0°, 90°, 180°, etc. Mat is higher in compressive strength than fabric. In multiple layers it has less tendency to delaminate when stressed to the failure point. And, very important to the builder, mat will bond better between its interply layers and can be effectively used to build section thickness and obtain resultant panel stiffness. While mat will adapt to more complicated shapes than fabric, its handling and surface-finish characteristics are sometimes a drawback.

Strand deposited with a chopper gun yields a reinforcement with characteristics equivalent to mats. The only important factor is whether the manually operated gun can achieve as consistent a uniformity as the mats which are made on an automated machine.

Fabric is by far the most expensive reinforcement on a pound basis. It also exhibits the highest tensile and flexural strengths, but, as mentioned before, only in the direction of strand orientation. The impact strength in a heavy woven roving laminate is decidedly higher than a laminate laid up with mat or even sheer fabric. But fabric laminates do show relative inter-ply weakness under maximum stress. Fabrics help provide uniform thickness control in contact molding and contribute to high glass density in a laminate. The lighter grades are widely used to provide an even surface finish.

One question which comes up often is, "What effect does fiber length have on strength?" Some people are under the impression that the longer the fiber, the stronger the laminate will be; hence, fabric reinforcements are entirely superior. Part of the answer is given in the foregoing discussion, but it should be pointed out that in the case of cut-fiber laminates, which might be made with mat, no specific strength fall-off will be seen until the fiber length is reduced below approximately one-half inch. In other words, in chopped fiber laminate, no strength advantage is gained by using a one-or two-inch fiber over about three-quarter inch length.

Application of Physical Properties

The determination of when and where to employ these several reinforcement materials can become quite complex if strict theory is carried to its end point. However, a few simple principles are the truly important factors in making a good quality laminate.

The first point is that the glass content is a more controlling factor on specific strengths in contact molding than the exact form of reinforcement. The result is that cloth, which is a more compact or dense form of reinforcement, contributes higher glass loading. Another major advantage to cloth is its high degree of uniformity.

Mat, cloth or woven roving can be used singly or in combination to build hull structures. Each of the materials has its advantages and its weaknesses; the common practice today is to combine the materials to get the best out of each.

Typical Laminate Combinations

Laminates made exclusively with cloth are not common for boat construction because of cost. Woven roving is generally used in combination with mat. The mat compliments the roving by hiding the coarse weave pattern, improves the bond between layers of roving and builds bulk for thickness. In the case of woven roving laminates (two layers), the mat may serve the function of a water gasket seal.

The exclusive use of chopped fiber or mat is favored by certain builders, and proof of its adequacy can be made by pointing to the many successful small boats and a few very large hulls that have been built with this reinforcement. Generally speaking, woven roving and mat combination laminates are more common, the mat type construction being preferred by a few builders who are especially capable in working with the material.

In the case of relatively thin panels, where the coarse woven roving is not needed or desirable, a layer of mat may be sandwiched between surface plies of cloth. Such construction is used in light hull shells and component parts.

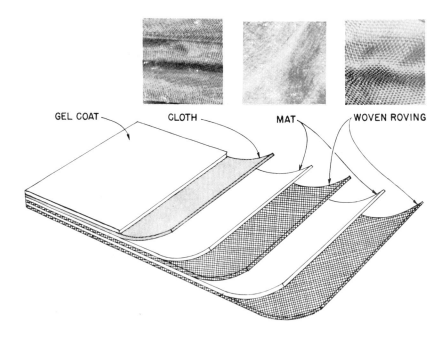

GEL COAT   CLOTH   MAT   WOVEN ROVING

Surface-finish appearance has a determining influence on the choice of reinforcement used. Some builders use a cloth layer directly behind exterior gel coat of resin, others prefer a chopped or mat fiber which has less tendency to show through. A layer of fine cloth is sometimes used on the interior surface to impart a neater appearance. The waffle grid effect from the woven roving is commonly seen on the interior of hulls. The masking of this pattern on the exterior is done by a number of molding techniques, but a layer of mat plays an important part in hiding the heavy fabric.

Special finishes or sizes are applied to the fiberglass in order that the resin will achieve an intimate bond to the glass surface and thereby yield maximum laminate strengths.

It may be helpful to describe in detail the manner in which a typical small-boat laminate is developed and why each form of glass material is selected. For illustration, we will pick a combination laminate about three-sixteenths-inch thick that might be required in a 15′ outboard boat made by contact molding.

Fiberglass boats are built "outside-in" when using the common contact lay-up system. The first operation is to apply a color coat of resin about 13 to 20 mils thick in the cavity mold. Next comes a layer of glass which performs the function of backing up and reinforcing the color coat. Often the material selected is a light fabric which is carefully smoothed and worked out so that it gives an even void-free support to the exterior resin coat. Mat or chopped fiber may also be selected to do this job. Some builders prefer the latter because it has less tendency to show a fiber pattern. Next in sequence might be a layer of fiberglass mat which gives bulk and rigidity to the laminate. While this resin-saturated mat is still wet, a layer of heavy woven roving fabric is pressed against it. This heavy fabric is selected for its high impact strength and uniformity. To finish the hull shell off, another layer of the heavy fabric may be added, depending on the strength requirements. Some builders will interleaf a layer of mat between the layers of woven roving in order to add thickness and improve the bond between the coarse fabrics.

Thus, each type of reinforcement has its particular physical properties and purpose. Any number of design and process factors enter into choosing a suitable reinforcement, among which strength and cost are only two. It can be seen from this discussion, which gives some insight into the reasons why and how different reinforcements are used, that it is not possible to advise on the best type or the best combination unless a very specific hull structure is under consideration.

CHAPTER 3

Construction—Molding Processes

THE OPEN MOLD, contact layup system has proven to be the universally accepted method for fiberglass hull production. In the early days of the business a variety of relatively complex molding techniques were employed involving heat, pressure, vacuum injection and so forth. Out of all this applied process engineering only the matched die method has proven to be an acceptable alternative to the contact system, and essentially the matched die process is limited to very high volume production of small simple hulls. Car top outboards like the Sears Gamefisher are a good example.

Matched Metal Die Molding

The Molded Fiberglass Boat Co., Union City, Pa., was the first to attempt matched die molding of boats. Goodyear Aircraft shortly followed, but did not stay in the business. Producing a 15', 150-lb. hull shell in a single, hydraulic press cycle is no mean feat. It is exceedingly dramatic to see a limp, characterless mass of fiberglass and resin draped over the mold and then transformed in one swift closure of the press into a smooth, seamless hull. Considering the apparent rapidity of this production system the reader may logically ask why such a manufacturing technique does not greatly reduce the cost of boats. There are probably two answers to this question. In the first place, the hull shell as it comes off the press is a long way from being a completed boat. Many other parts such as keel, stiffeners, deck, thwarts, etc., still have to be added. Secondly, the production volume in any one model is not sufficiently large to run it around the clock through the year and achieve maximum utilization of the production equipment.

Contact Pressure Molding

The popular production method used in the industry, where any reasonable volume of production is entertained, is contact pressure molding. This involves a fiberglass cavity mold that is formed on a male form of wood or plaster called a "plug." The plug is an exact facsimile of the part to be built, and in many cases is considered expendable. After curing, the mold is removed from the plug and multiple layers of

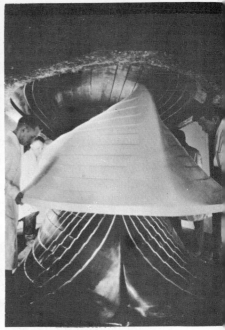

Left--In contact pressure molding layers of fiberglass matting and fabric are progressively applied—each layer is saturated with resin—technique of "layup" men is important to insure uniform consistency of the laminate. Right--Lapstrake shell emerging from matched die metal molds.

fiberglass, saturated with resin, are built up in the cavity and allowed to cure to a hardened state without heat or pressure. The lay-up system is relatively simple and much less expensive than a tool steel die. Capital investment in molds and equipment is relatively low, short production runs are possible, and even "in-season" mold changes are practical. Single hull and deck moldings over 100-feet long can be handled. (Matched die molding is probably limited to 20-feet.)

Contact pressure molding has a number of important advantages during "in process" stage. Since the whole hull or deck laminate is at all times visible, defects such as air bubbles or dry spots can be immediately seen and corrected. The result is that any well-run contact molding shop has few rejects. Extra reinforcing layers of material can be readily applied as needed. Stiffening members and components such as bulkheads, flooring, and so on can be bonded in place in an efficiently programmed sequence.

All the large fiberglass powerboats are built up in cavity molds and are molded in surprisingly few sections. The Hatteras 41, for instance, is done fundamentally in three molded components—the hull, the entire deck and cabin structure, and the flying bridge unit. Of course, there are a dozen or more subsidiary molds which produce ventilators, hatches, etc. Other builders prefer to break the superstructure up into more parts, perhaps for shop-handling reasons or to offer alternate model arrangements. Since sections of cured fiberglass laminate can be easily bonded, or let's say welded together, the builder can work out the assembly procedure in any number of ways.

Plugs

The plug, over which the fiberglass cavity mold is formed, can be constructed in a number of ways. Because woodworking technology seems to be understood throughout the country and, particularly, in the marine field, it is common to see this basic material used for mold plugs. The master shape is built up with planks over mold frame stations after which the surface is carefully worked down to proper tolerance by planing and sanding. Since any type of imperfection will be faithfully transferred to the cavity mold and difficult to correct, considerable care goes into final surface preparation of the plug.

A number of special techniques are used to obtain a stable, high-gloss finish. Some tool makers cover the wooden plug with fiberglass boat cloth and polyester resin and then meticulously grind and polish this reinforced sheathing. A quicker and more popular technique involves the use of special plastic surfacing compounds applied directly to the wooden surface without the glass reinforcement. A wooden mold so treated will not remain crack-free indefinitely, but with proper care will last long enough to serve its function.

The art of developing plaster plugs for boats seems to be quite common in certain parts of the country. Mechanics skilled in this technique will be found in the midwestern areas where a majority of the automotive and machine-tool industries are located. The chief advantage to this system is the ease of fairing and smoothing down the plaster surface. The difficult operation is the somewhat tricky technique of building up the plaster mold. Some experience is needed to learn how to handle the wet plaster properly as the plaster plugs are heavy and subject to breakage. Although the use of the material in this country appears to be confined to developing small craft in the outboard category, we do know that very large plaster plugs have been built sucessfully in other countries. As an example, Alan Payne, designer of the Australian Cup challenger, told the writer that large plaster developments are often done in his country and that he had supervised the building of a plaster mold for a 40' auxiliary of his design.

Chopper Gun Depositor

While contact pressure molding and matched metal die molding are the two systems currently popular in fiberglass boat production, there is a later development known as the fiber-resin chopper gun depositor which is regarded by many as a third system. Actually, we prefer to regard it as a production tool, and classify it in the contact-molding category. Conventional contact molding utilizes layers of fiberglass fabric and/or matting which are saturated with polyester resin by spray gun or brush. A chopper gun depositor simultaneously shoots chopped fiberglass strand and polyester resin into the boat mold. The method has proved

Plug development for Hatteras 41 shown in sequence. Top—Mold stations set up. Center—Strip planking complete. Bottom—Wood form has received fiberglass cloth and resin and is being sanded fair. Finished plug will be glass smooth. Black pigmented resin shows up high spots and depressions.

Photos from Hatteras Yacht Co.

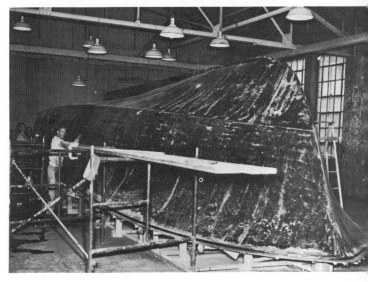

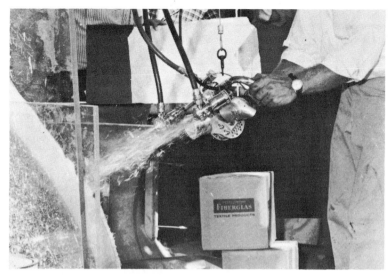

The Rand chopper gun depositor simultaneously
deposits resin and cut fiberglass.

particularly adaptable where rapid lay-up of complex shapes is involved and where the forming and fitting of a matting or fabric are difficult.

The gun depositor, however, needs careful handling so uniformity of fiber dispersion and resin catalyzation is assured. It cannot be considered a true and complete molding system unless proper controls are applied. Quality manufacturers, experienced in its use, employ a series of devices that control the amount of glass, resin and catalyst discharged through the apparatus.

Except for the chopper gun depositor, no new boat molding processes have been developed in the past few years. There have, however, been a significant number of refinements worked out in the contact molding system. The method has been automated to a large degree by the outboard-boat producers who turn out a large volume. Some assembly-line techniques can be seen in the new plants; operations are carefully timed and programmed; and resin handling systems have been vastly improved. Instead of resin being carried to a mold in a pail and applied with a brush, for example, it may be piped in from a reservoir tank and applied with a spray gun. Advances in polyester resin technology have taken place and have had a great deal to do with the speeding up of production without sacrificing the desirable properties in the laminate. But what the future will bring to boat molding processes is hard to say.

1

Various stages in the construction of a fiberglass boat as seen at the Nashville, Tenn., plant of The Glasspar Co. 1. Tough, resilient color-impregnated polyester resin being sprayed into the cavity mold of a 16-foot Glasspar outboard hull. This color coat is 10 times thicker than a coat of normal marine paint and becomes an integral part of the hull laminate. 2. A layer of heavy glass fabric is smoothed in place in the mold. The hull or deck shell is essentially a built-up sandwich of resin-impregnated fiberglass. The thickness will vary according to design factors and internal framing which will be installed later. 3. Layup in the deck mold proceeds in the same fashion as with the hull. Exceedingly complex deck features can be molded in one seamless shape. 4. Hull shell is popped free from cavity mold after sufficient time for cure has elapsed. While this shell has the appearance of an almost completed boat, it will still spend considerable time in subassembly departments.

Chattanooga "News-Free Press"

2

3

4

The Mold Cost Problem

A cavity mold, regardless of the materials used or the method in which it is built, will be a relatively high-cost fixture. As has been stated, a master plug is first built and then a fiberglass cavity is formed over the male plug. On a commercial basis, it is estimated that ten hulls are necessary to properly amortize this type of tooling. The cost can be easily amortized or absorbed if a builder is producing, say, 40 or 50 boats. For very short production runs, this development cost becomes a factor to be carefully considered. In large hull construction, ten units are generally the minimum volume that can be undertaken unless the yacht buyers are willing to absorb a significant portion of the mold expense.

As we proceed into the development of very large fiberglass yachts, where the potential market for any one design is extremely small, mold costs become an increasingly important factor. It is apparent that low-cost mold systems are needed where only one or two large hull reproductions are considered.

Inexpensive Cavity Mold Techniques

There has been some attention directed to cavity molds which are less costly than the commercial system previously discussed. The technique so far successfully employed involves planking up a cavity directly within female mold stations. The method is not unlike the "down east" technique of building wooden ship planked hulls. Masonite and thin mahogany veneer have been used for the mold sheathing.

The starboard cavity mold has been removed to reveal the graceful hull lines of an Alden 38' yawl. Note molded in cove stripe and detail of deadwood section where ballast will be added.

The mold cavities have been slid back from the suspended hull. This construction by Halmatic Ltd. faithfully transfers every design detail to the finished hull.

Startling in its size, the Alden 67' Ocean Commander emerges from her split cavity mold at the Halmatic plant. The polished plywood mold surfaces maintain their condition in an air conditioned mold room.

The Halmatic Co. in England, for instance, builds up the mold face with thin sheets of wood veneer plywood or untempered Masonite, and arrives at a beautifully smooth, fair hull surface. (Such materials are much less expensive than fiberglass-plastic.) Their wood construction is carefully done and the process favored by an air-conditioned plant which minimizes expansion and contraction of the wood. It is true that these molds are not very durable, but with care they can remain serviceable for several lay-ups. Significant reduction in mold costs can be achieved by this system.

It can be understood that if a gel coat is not employed and a certain amount of surface rework is accepted, a cavity mold of fine finish and dimension is not required. There have been a number of fine auxiliaries molded in simply developed cavities. The decision really reduces itself to whether to expend the effort finishing the mold or the actual part. The late Stewart Forbes of Gloucester, Mass., who pioneered such a technique on a 40' powerboat of displacement design, reported that his mold cost him not much more than $3,000. Mr. Forbes used untempered Masonite formed against set-up wooden stations. The hull shell came free from the mold with excellent fairness and very little exterior rework. A fiberglass production mold of that size, produced in the conventional manner, might run five to eight times that figure.

Male Mold Techniques

The question, then, is: "What tooling procedure is best if only one hull or part is required?" At this stage of development we think that a simple male plug is the answer. Quite a few successful large and small fiberglass boats have been built in this fashion.

The advantage to the male mold system is that only one forming fixture is needed. A light, inexpensively constructed wooden framework can be used. After the fiberglass shell has been laminated over this surface it is not too difficult to sand and fair the convex shape to get a smooth finish. It will certainly take a considerable number of man hours to machine the outside of the shell, but this is not nearly so difficult as fairing and finishing a cavity contour.

Wood is the popular material for such a male mold. The type will depend largely on the design to be developed. Narrow strip planks or veneer have been used for contoured shapes. Plywood and Masonite panels serve well for flat planes or simple curves. Inexpensive woods are desirable, but not so cheap that accuracy of the shell is jeopardized.

Male molds are generally only used once, and then scrapped, but some have been used several times.

It is certain that much progress will be made in the next few years on solving the "one off" problem. The interest and demand for fiberglass vessels in the 100' range is rapidly emerging from military and commercial sources. One can perhaps say that it will always be cheaper to build a large yacht hull from wood than in fiberglass because of the mold cost, but on the other hand, the hull mold becomes a relatively small portion of the total expense when a big, elaborately equipped yacht is considered.

Integral Mold Techniques

The U.S. Navy has spent a considerable amount of money in researching minimum mold cost techniques for fiberglass boats, as their procurement programs often call for only one, two, or three of a particular design. This is especially true in lengths above 45'. Because they also have been interested in using sandwich construction in the fiberglass structure, they have investigated materials which serve the dual purpose of a mold form and a core around which the fiberglass is laminated.

Quite a number of fiberglass navy craft have been constructed using honeycomb or foamed plastic planks as a mold core. The principle is quite simple. In the case of the honeycomb core, a battened framework form is erected and the glass skin laminated over the honeycomb. After cure the half-molded structure is lifted off the battened mold stations, turned over, and the inside skin is laminated in place. This "sandwich" construction will be discussed in the next chapter.

At this point it is fair to point out that these stressed-skin or core hulls have some favorable advantages, but they also induce certain problems which have not been solved. In short, it is best to say that the theory is correct, but that the present selection of suitable core materials imposes limits on achieving maximum results. Because interest in larger fiberglass hulls is on the increase, it is certain that these problems will yield to technical advances in the next few years.

24

BUILDING A STOCK FIBERGLASS CRUISER

Hull Molding and Construction

The Commander's hull form has two readily observed unique features—a full length molded quarter foil and a slightly V'd transom. In addition, as seen in photographs 2 and 3, she has recessed portlights and a sheer which is rolled inward. One can visualize that with these rather special shapes, the hull shell cannot be laid up in or pulled free from an ordinary single cavity mold. Chris-Craft engineers designed and built a special mold to make this possible. It is not shown here because of the rather proprietary nature of this development.

In photographs number B and 1 we see the basic hull suspended from chain hoists preparatory to sand-blasting the bottom. The scouring action of the sand blast insures proper adhesion of the anti-fouling paint.

In photograph 3 the hulls start down the assembly line where they will receive interior joinery work, engines, superstructure and so on. This particular photograph shows a number of interesting structural features. The molded gunwale that rolls inward contributes considerable strength and stiffness to the hull shell. The deck molding shown in photograph 4 is bonded and mechanically fastened to this flange that runs the full length of the shear and completely around the transom.

A further look at photograph 3 reveals an interesting arrangement of stiffeners, transverse floors and engine bed stringers. Most of these

B—A 38-foot Commander has just emerged from the mold room sus-pended from chain hoists. Bottom will be sandblasted and painted.

25

1—Unique, full length, quarter foil V'd transom and concave planing surfaces are evident from this photo angle (left). 2—Special tooling permits recessed bow port light. Note high gloss gel coat from finely polished molds.

3—Commander hulls move down the assembly line parallel with wooden hulls. 4—Molded deck before attachment to hull (right).

members are hollow fiberglass hat sections. There are more of these stringers in the Commander than in other comparable fiberglass hulls for a rather special reason. The basic hull is designed to accommodate a number of different interior hull arrangements. The Chris-Craft engineers wanted to have a hull structure independently self-supporting and not in any way relying on interior bulkheads or similar components, which is common practice in other glass powerboats. It is inter-

5—Cabin top moldings ready to be installed (left). 6—Pilothouse top seen upside-down. It involves two molded pieces.

7—Cockpit molding with opening for hatch. 8—Male mold (right) for cockpit. Such detailed molds require much time, skill and expense.

esting to point out too that the full length quarter foil is boxed in on the interior and in itself serves as a fine stiffening member for the topsides.

Deck and Superstructure

In photographs 4 through 8 the primary deck and superstructure moldings are shown. All these large flat parts are stiffened by a full

27

9—Above left—Pilothouse top is mounted and supported by aluminum members.

10—Above—Metal support of pilothouse top is shrouded by fiberglass panel.

11—Left—Molded window channel in pilothouse.

sandwich core of 1/2" plywood. The cabin top and the pilothouse top have additional widely spaced firring strips or carlins to which the fabric head liners can be fastened.

Photographs 7 and 8 show the cockpit and the actual mold from which it is produced. The picture of the mold is shown to give an idea of type of tool fixture which is needed to produce such a finely-detailed, precisely fitting part. The mold is constructed of fiberglass-reinforced polyester, backed up with wood and steel and mounted on casters so that it can be moved around the shop.

Some Assembly Detail

Some of the photographs next under discussion are a bit obscure but some details of assembly should be shown. An initial reaction of "what-is-it" will yield to understanding after brief study.

Photographs 9 and 10 show the mounting of the pilothouse top to the cabin top using aluminum channels which also accept the windshield. In photograph 10 the internal aluminum support surrounded by the fiberglass fairing panel is shown.

In photograph 11 the camera moves in close to show the molded channel which accepts the sliding pilothouse glass. This detail treatment

12—Interior woodwork is fastened to fiberglass cabin trunk shell (left). 13—Heavy fiberglass longitudinal and transverse members support engines (right).

14—Freedom of design in fiberglass results in handsome sink-counter molding (left). 15—Foam insulated fiberglass icebox is poduced from wooden plug form (above).

is interesting because it is a trouble point on wooden hulls and Chris-Craft uses this molded fiberglass channel on their new wooden models as well as the Commander.

Photograph 12 shows some important, but perhaps unglamorous detailing. The view is from the inside looking through the forward trunk cabin windshield. Mahogany panels have been bonded and fastened to the fiberglass shell. Visible too is the aluminum window center post, which also serves as one of supporting members for the cabin roof. At the top of the photo can be seen the plywood-cored ceiling before the fabric headliners have been attached.

16—Plywood panels for stiffening cores in deck and superstructure.

17—

Photograph 13 shows the engine bed mounting arrangement. The engine is fastened to heavy wooden members which are securely fiberglassed to the longitudinal hat-shaped stringers.

Photographs 14 and 15 show two neatly designed interior components: the lavatory sink and the refrigerator. Chris-Craft has molded these types of parts for many years. In photograph 15 the actual fiberglass box liner with heavy foam insulation is seen on the right and the wooden male mold fixture is on the left.

30

Photograph 16, which shows the plywood panels for stiffening cores in deck and superstructure, is confirmation of the fact that a considerable amount of wood is used in most fiberglass boats. These are pre-cut, plywood panels. Notice the shallow depth saw cuts which allow the plywood to be formed in place more easily. The plywood is placed in the cavity mold against the outerskin of fiberglass, then further laminations of glass are applied over the plywood. The result is a relatively thick, stiff panel which will resist deflection and still be relatively light. Lighter core materials like Balsa are sometimes used, but plywood has the advantage of higher strength and good fiber density to hold the screw fasteners securely.

In photo 17 a completed Commander at the end of the assembly line in the Roamer plant is shown. The flying bridge is temporarily in place, but will be transported in the cockpit during truck delivery. The handsome shape of the hull is evident in this perspective shot. Notice the low speed spray deflector which runs back a short distance from the stem.

The nicely styled sheer and cabin profile are shown in photo 18. Many fiberglass cabin trunks tend to have a molded look. In the Commander there is a straight line, crisp styling which is emphasized by the use of narrow aluminum support channels and trim. Note the engineroom ventilator scoop which is neatly mounted on the teak sheer cap.

The Chris-Craft designers have devoted considerable research to improving visibility from the helm. Hull speeds have increased greatly and adequate visibility for the helmsman at all times is increasingly important. The aluminum framed center break windshield as shown in photo 19 is strong and tight and blends nicely with the fiberglass.

The large molded fiberglass pilot console is shown in photo 20. This is one of the earliest fiberglass applications used by Chris-Craft and thus it shows a great deal of refinement. The center section, for instance, is given

18—Photo at left below emphasizes the size and proportions of the fiberglass Commander 38. Clean deck lines are distinctive. 19—Aluminum frame windshield (below right) is a classic, proved design. Flying bridge is optional.

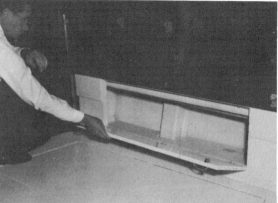

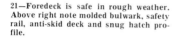
20—Fiberglass steering console (above left) is focal point in the pilothouse. Chris-Craft offers a specially-designed wheel and instrument panel.

21—Foredeck is safe in rough weather. Above right note molded bulwark, safety rail, anti-skid deck and snug hatch profile.

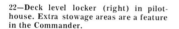
22—Deck level locker (right) in pilothouse. Extra stowage areas are a feature in the Commander.

texture by means of a special transfer material in the mold. An aluminum pillaster extrusion will be noticed just above and to the left of the helm. There is one of these support columns on each side of the pilothouse. The wiring and steering cables leading to the flying bridge run through these members.

Photo 21 shows the foredeck. Notice the low molded bulwark capped with a teak plate. This styling detail does much to enhance the appearance of the boat. The stanchions are lagged through the teak cap, through the molded deck and into a back-up plate of plywood. The deck surface has a molded anti-skid finish. The bitt is a solid teak member that extends downward to join with the stem. It must be pointed out that the hatch is a very nice design—in aluminum.

Photo 22 shows a handy locker at floor level on the starboard side in the pilothouse. The box section in the center is an air duct for the engineroom, the cowl of which is shown in photo 2.

Storage space as well as living space is increased in fiberglass hulls as compared to wooden construction.

Photo 23 shows the folding hatch arrangement which affords excellent access to the engines. There are four panel segments and a removable center bar. The hatch opening is large enough so that engine replacement is greatly facilitated.

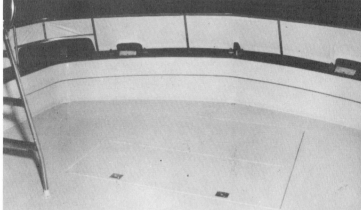

23—With hatches opened, engines are completely accessible. Segmental folding arrangement is convenient.

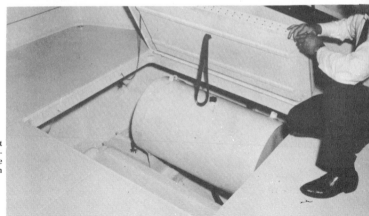

24—Molded cockpit decking and wainscot is functional.

25—After hatch is built of two solid folding sections. Large stowage area is available beneath cockpit sole.

26—Molded quarter foil sweeps around transom. Cockpit scupper drains and exhaust ports are vented on the underside.

27—Sample of the copper radiotelephone ground screen (left). 28—Grounding screen (right) is molded into the bottom of 27-foot hull. Screen is laminated behind the gel coat.

Photos 24 and 25 show the after portion of the cockpit and its hatch detail. The cockpit deck is molded fiberglass with an anti-skid pattern. Dirt does not get trapped in the rounded corners, and the whole section including the hatches has adequate scuppers. The floor is heavily constructed of a plywood-cored laminate reinforced with wooden transverse beams. Above the engine compartment there is thick insulation. The result is a rigid, sound-dampening structure. The after hatch in photo 25 gives easy access to a large storage area. One of the galvanized steel fuel tanks can be seen through the opening.

Photo 26 shows the unique V'd stern and transom in detail. The engine and gasoline generator exhaust ports can be seen on the underside of the molded quarter foil. The flared keel is visible as well as the molded-in wedges. Photos 27 and 28 involve a mysterious and intriguing bit of electronic engineering. They concern the radiotelephone grounding system. Non-conductive hulls like wood and fiberglass need an adequate ground plate for assorted marine electronic gear.

As power output has increased, the need for a ground fixture of sufficient area and efficiency has grown too. Photo 27 shows a special grounding screen which Chris-Craft has developed in co-operation with Bendix engineers. The copper screen is not woven! It is extruded. This particular unit is 12 sq. ft. in area and is sufficient for a 130 watt transmitter. Installation is interesting. The screen is molded into the bottom of the hull. It is actually interleaved into the laminate, behind the layer of glass cloth which backs up the gel coat. Apparently it is not necessary to have the copper in direct contact with the water. Photo 28 shows the screen being laminated into the bottom of the new 27;footer. The broad, copper conductor lead is taken up the side of the hull.

Chris-Craft engineers say the same grounding system can be used in wooden hulls, and they have established a method of sandwiching the screen between the layers of double planking.

TOURING A FIBERGLASS PLANT

Jensen Marine has a modern production facility for auxiliary sailing yachts

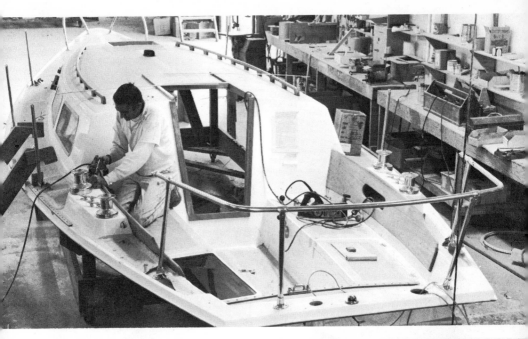

Above: Exterior hardware and fittings are installed before the deck is mated to the hull, while both sides of the deck are completely accessible.

Right: One-piece hull and "dead wood" molding is separated from the mold with water pressure, then lifted free. Boottop and sheer striping are in gel coat.

Above left: Cockpit and deck mold ready for the lay-up procedure. Cockpit, seat hatches, waterways and deck transfer pattern are visible on complicated tool. Above right: Multiple laminations of heavyweight glass cloth are carefully formed in place by hand on the mold, each being laid in wet resin. This woven roving material varies in thickness according to strength requirements.

Above left: Fiberglass hull cavity mold is polished to mirror finish before laminating process begins. It's a painstaking job, for every detail is faithfully transferred to the hull surface. Above right: Underside of deck, which is not in contact with the mold, is ground fair with sander. Deck may be cored with plywood to build up the stiffness.

Below left: Transverse wooden structural members are assembled and installed while hull is still in mold, preventing distortion that could occur if bare shell were removed. Glass cloth lapping mold edge is easily trimmed. Below right: Joinery is assembled in logical units, then dropped in and fiberglassed to the hull. Auxiliary engine is the last major installation before deck is added.

Above left: Pair of spade rudders get final sanding before installation.
Above right: Thorough detailing and touching up in last production steps.

BUILT TO TAKE IT—

AN OCEAN-GOING 75 FOOT FIBERGLASS YACHT

CUSTOM FIBERGLASS YACHTS are not unknown but they are rare enough compared to those constructed with wood, steel or aluminum. Fiberglass is identified with today's stock boat business. Many people assume that because of the need for molds and their attendant cost that the material is unsuitable for "one of a kind" yacht construction.

The 75-foot motor yacht shown in the accompanying photographs, and the Willard Boat Co. who built her, offer a convincing case for fiberglass hulls in this highly specialized field.

Over the years a scattered number of one-of-a-kind fiberglass yachts have been built. However, in most cases, these have been somewhat experimental projects undertaken to satisfy singular requirements. Few have led the way into the establishment of a fiberglass custom yacht business. It is this aspect which is perhaps most notable about the Willard Boat Co.

As long-time builders of wooden yachts, the Willard people turned to fiberglass in 1959. Their initial offering was a William Garden-designed, conventionally tooled 36-ft. trawler yacht. The company soon realized that their wood craftsmanship was of particular value in building molds, and this, combined with other associated capabilities, persuaded them to avoid a stock hull line that would put them in hard competition with so many other southern California fiberglass boat builders. They chose instead to concentrate on developing construction methods which could be used for the production of single and limited series fiberglass yachts. The decision appears to have been a sound one.

To date Willard has built over 50 custom yacht hulls. Proficiency with materials and methods has improved from year to year, permitting them to take on ever larger and more complex designs.

Fresh from mold, hull shell reveals powerful lines
and extremely fair finish.

Above: Profile view of cavity
mold displays framing and planking arrangement.

Left: Careful fabrication and
alignment of mold stations are
important steps.

Above left: Plywood planking of the starboard portion of the mold proceeds with considerable speed.
Above right: Joints, fastenings and surface defects are filled and sanded.

Above: Layer of glass cloth and polyester resin is applied to stabilize the plywood surface.

Right: After further applications of resin filler, surface is worked to final finish by electric sanding and buffing.

The success which the Willard people have gained in this specialized field is not attributable to any revolutionary technique in working with fiberglass materials. Rather, they have tailored and refined certain construction practices to meet the particular requirements. In approaching a custom yacht program they do not dismiss the tooling cost burden nor do they employ short-cut methods which might jeopardize necessary quality standards. In their minds it is a matter of properly relating process methods, materials and resultant costs to the job at hand. The circumstances do tend to be somewhat different from one custom hull project to another.

Today's conventional tooling system for series production of molded hulls involves building a wooden plug from which a fiberglass cavity mold is then developed, two relatively expensive fabrication steps. For hulls above 25 feet, it is customary to amortize such tooling costs over a minimum of eight or ten units. However, in the Willard system, two modifications effect significant cost savings. Number one, they proceed directly to a cavity mold and eliminate the entire plug phase. Secondly, they utilize lightweight, rapidly assembled, low-cost materials in the construction of the cavity mold.

By specific description, the cavity is developed by planking carefully set up mold stations with plywood or possibly masonite. Certain areas of complex shape may need fitted strip planking. A smooth hard mold surface is achieved by a proprietary plastic compound reinforced with glass cloth. While the basic system allows them to step around some of the more costly procedures inherent in conventional tooling, a high degree of skill and experience is required to obtain the necessary quality of workmanship for a custom yacht.

The mold is lightly constructed, yet is rugged enough to produce two or perhaps three copies without any significant rework. One might describe it as "disposable" tooling, but that isn't too accurate a description because the system has produced molds with a surprising reuse life.

Cost of Mold Relative to Total Cost of Yacht

It can readily be appreciated that custom construction of any kind today is expensive and costs continue to rise as the necessary type of skilled craftsmen becomes more difficult to find. In the case of any well-built, well-found custom yacht the cost of the hull alone will not represent a high percentage of the fitted-out price. The situation is really irrespective of the hull material costs and behooves the owner to specify top quality throughout the structure.

In actuality then, the cost of the Willard mold system is not negligible, but it is reduced to a manageable proportion in relation to total economic outlay for a custom yacht. Successful and confident in their approach to this business, the Willard management state that they can produce a custom fiberglass yacht which is competitive in cost with quality wood, steel or aluminum construction.

There is also an important business aspect which gives an opportunity for mold amortization. As a rule, the owner will be responsible for the cost of the tool. But the matter does not end there. He and/or the builder can usually interest one or two individuals in the same basic hull and thus spread the tooling charge. Other variations in mold ownership and write-off are possible. The important point is that when dealing with good design and quality workmanship, molds can become an investment which is negotiable.

Mold modifications extend hull use

The Willard people have demonstrated the capability of making certain alterations to hull molds so that quite different design configurations can be achieved. Such versatility is highly important with larger hulls and obviously assists economic considerations.

For example, some of their designs can be lengthened as much as ten feet when worked out within the government beam-length radio. This can be implemented by a demountable transom section of the mold. Several years ago the mold for a 65-ft. sightseeing design was modified to a trawler-yacht configuration by the use of simple molding stops to reduce the sheer to proper height.

FURTHER SPECIFICATIONS, WILLARD 75
POWER TRAIN: G. M. 12V-71N SHP-482 each @ 2,300 RPM
Twin Disc 2:1, 2½" monel shafts
SPEED: 14 knots cruise, 16 knots max.
RANGE: 3,000 miles max., 1,200 miles @ 14 knots
TANKS: Fuel - 4,000 gals., aluminum
Water - 500 gals., stainless
Augmented by Maxim HJ3 watermaker, 190 gals./day
CONSTRUCTION MATERIALS: One piece molded fiberglass hull, combination mat and woven roving—gel coat exterior finish. Full-length fiberglass longitudinals. Hull shell thicknesses, stem, keel and chines to 2½", bottom to 1½", topsides to ¾". Superstructure, laminated fiberglass over plywood.
DECKS: Burma teak over fiberglass
TRIM AND BRIGHTWORK: Pecan, teak and mahogany.,
SPARS: (2) molded fiberglass.

CHAPTER 4

Core—Sandwich Construction

THE STRUCTURE IN A fiberglass boat is seldom developed exclusively with fiberglass and resin, except perhaps in small simple craft like dinghies. In anything larger there are often complementary, non-glass-resin materials incorporated in the hull or deck. The purpose of this chapter is to discuss why so-called "core materials" are used in fiberglass construction, what kinds are employed, and how they should be regarded by the boat owner.

Theory and Purpose of Core Construction

As mentioned in a previous chapter, a fiberglass laminate has a lower modulus of stiffness than other materials like wood and metals. In simple terms, it is more flexible. By taking advantage of natural curves in the design, adequate stiffness may be provided. In other cases, the design weight may allow a solution through increase of shell thickness. More often, however, the builder or designer compensates for this characteristic by the use of longitudinal or rib stiffeners; or he may elect to develop a "sandwich" hull or deck shell to provide rigidity. These two basic systems can be used singly or in combination. Both engineering methods have produced successful boats.

When using the "sandwich" or "core" system, a light, suitable material is placed between two fiberglass skins so that the section stiffness of the panel is increased without undue addition of weight. This sounds simple but the difficulty arises in selecting the proper material for the job. The problem of selecting a good core material involves cost, strength, durability and process adaptability. The characteristics will be discussed as these qualifications relate to each core material now in actual use in fiberglass boats.

Wood Cores

Wood is one of the oldest construction materials. It is versatile, generally economic, and there is wide understanding of its properties and how it can be processed. Modern forms such as plywood and pressed fiberboard have opened up important new end uses.

Plywood is widely used wood core material in fiberglass boat construction. Typically, it will be found incorporated in the transoms of outboard boats and in decks of larger craft. Very often the design is such that the plywood is actually the load-carrying member of the combination, the thinner glass-plastic shell serving as a protective envelope.

Balsa cores are most accepted today in deck and cabin structures of auxiliaries and power cruisers. Several years back a good many fiberglass outboard producers were using balsa sandwich hull bottoms. This technique, however, has given way to some degree to foam sandwich and to single-skin bottoms suitably stiffened with hollow glass ribs and longitudinals.

The advantage of balsa is that it makes a much lighter core than plywood. A number of builders develop large compound-curved sandwich forms by using small pieces. The balsa pieces are placed against the inside surface of the outer shell while it is still in the mold. The loose aggregation of diced balsa is fused into a unified core by the encompassing fiberglass skins.

While plywood and balsa have proven most acceptable and popular for the builders, other wood type cores have been successfully employed. Masonite and similar kinds of pressed-pulp wood have worked satisfactorily; also glued-up wood veneers, where curved sections are developed.

Some Controversy About Wood Cores

Within the industry there have been differences of opinion as to where and how wood can be encapsulated in a fiberglass boat. Some feel that wood should be excluded entirely; others maintain that there are no problems or restrictions. The writer's opinion falls in between, not because the compromise position is more comfortable, but because we develop opinions from study and observations. In the last analysis, experience carries the most conclusive proof. Over a period of years, service use has clarified certain questions.

Encapsulation of hardwoods, either in the form of stringers or cores, has given trouble. Hard woods like oak may expand and crack the laminate. On the other hand, plywood is relatively stable and has a small coefficient of expansion. Balsa, a soft, compressible wood, seems to be

Fiberglass outboard transoms are commonly stiffened and strengthened with a core panel of marine grade plywood.

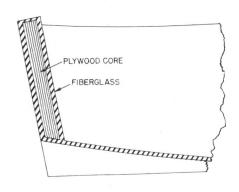

PLYWOOD CORE

FIBERGLASS

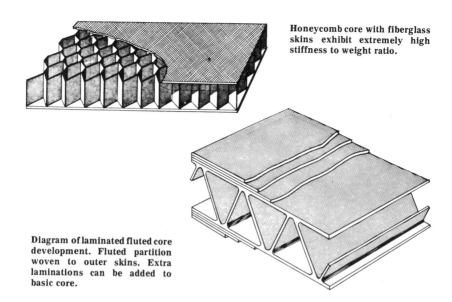

Honeycomb core with fiberglass skins exhibit extremely high stiffness to weight ratio.

Diagram of laminated fluted core development. Fluted partition woven to outer skins. Extra laminations can be added to basic core.

easily restrained by even quite thin skins of glass.

The question of rot has come up many times in the past, although not so frequently today. Results of laboratory and field experience are very encouraging. For instance, waterproof plywood transom cores have been used for more than a decade in outboards. No decomposition or rot has been found as long as the plywood has been properly sealed off from moisture and air. From laboratory checks it has also been found that the polyester resin and its catalyst systems have a quite poisonous effect on rot spores. No one has ranked these resins as full-fledged fungicides, but insofar as any rot-preventive solution is not permanently effective, resins are at least definitely helping to prevent occurence of rot.

The wood selected must be clean and dry, and respected wood-construction practices must be followed. Encapsulation of green wood or infected wood can be expected to cause rot problems.

Honeycomb Cores

Honeycomb cores were first used in the early days of fiberglass hull development. Experience in their usage has come to us from a variety of hull sizes and designs in military craft as well as small pleasure boats.

In general, performance has not lived up to expectation. Honeycomb is now only accepted for above-the-deck, panel-stiffening applications. Honeycomb cored hulls encountered problems with water migration through the cell structure and delamination of the skin faces from cell edges after impact blows. In spite of these problems in the hull, honeycomb sandwich techniques have worked well for deck and superstructure panels, where a high stiffness-to-weight ratio has been required.

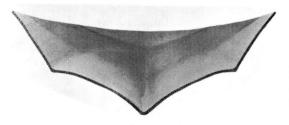

Bow section of outboard boat molded with fluted core, foam filled glass fabric.

Raymond Development Industries

Sponsored by the needs of other industries, honeycomb itself is offered in many material forms—aluminum, cotton duck, paper and fiberglass. Because of cost, only the paper type has received any serious interest in the marine field. The kraft-paper type exhibits good strength characteristics, and when heavily impregnated with phenolic resin is reasonably water-resistant.

A new variation on the honeycomb principle is shown in a photograph accompanying this chapter. It is a fluted-core glass fabric developed by the Raymond Development Co., of Huntington Park, Calif. This fabric innovation demonstrates striking ingenuity and should stimulate plastic engineers to come forth with some really interesting, high-performance fiberglass structures. The separating flutes and the glass skins are woven together in one simultaneous operation on the loom. The writer personally watched the weaving of this extraordinary material, but could not fathom how it is done. Needless to say, the Raymond people have obtained a patent on the material.

Raymond engineers have worked out some equally intriguing molding techniques. Compound curves are quite possible (as is seen in the bow section of the boat pictured). By the use of removable plastic inserts during the molding operation, a hollow-core system can be provided. By inserting preformed foam pieces in the unimpregnated fluted fabric, a foam glass sandwich can be developed.

Excellent physical strength has been exhibited with the Raymond fluted core system. Perhaps the most significant improvement over honeycomb panels results from the fact that flutes are woven to the outer skins so that there is a stronger bond between skin and core. Fluted core fabric is a high cost material, partly because it was originally designed for the aircraft industry to meet refined tolerances. Raymond engineers are working on other less expensive systems employing the same principle.

Foam Core System

Some of the most fascinating materials of this "plastics age" we live in are the synthetic foams. They are relatively new and extraordinarily versatile. Almost all plastic resins can be compounded into a foam consistency. We see them today used in a very wide variety of applications, from modern packaging systems and insulations to structures of various sorts.

As structural cores, foams are of great interest and potential to the fiberglass boat industry. In theory and in fact they are naturally complementary to fiberglass reinforced plastic structures. Now relatively new, foams can be expected to be improved and refined greatly in the next few years.

Thus far, the usage of foams in fiberglass boats has been rather confined to flotation applications and secondary structural support. A few small craft, like the well-known Boston Whaler, utilize foams in a primary structural manner. The great success of the Whaler and some other fully-foamed hulls demonstrate the true value and potential of the material.

Two Basic Methods

Foam sandwiches in fiberglass construction are currently made up in either of two basic methods. The older technique is to take preformed blocks or sheets of a suitable foam and laminate glass skins to the two surfaces. A more recent development has been the process of foaming in place between two preformed glass-reinforced polyester skins. This method permits the rapid fabrication of varying thicknesses and contours. It is the manner in which the complicated contours of the Boston Whaler are filled out with foam.

The future for foam plastics is very bright, but to gain wider acceptance and usage in structures a number of improvements have to be made. Cost is relatively high—about a dollar a cubic foot for expanded-in-place, two-pound density, urethane foam. Processing problems have been all too common. Sometimes large air pockets or distortion occur after it is foamed in place. Structural strength is inadequate for many purposes. Under severe abuse or impact, foams may fail under sheer stress while their high-density glass skins are still intact.

Microballoons

Technically classified as foams, but really different in nature, are a variety of hollow beads or pellets that can be compounded with resin to make strong rigid cores. The most successful type used so far for fiberglass boat construction has been phenolic microballoons made by Union Carbide Co. They are tiny, hollow spheres of phenolic resin containing nitrogen gas. The spheres are so small that they look and handle like a brown powder filler. Once mixed with an epoxy or polyester resin, the solidified compound forms a high-strength core material. It is a relatively high-density mix, usually up around 15-pounds per cubic foot, while the conventional foams are two to eight pounds in density.

Application of microballoons involves trowelling or "buttering" in place. Using this accepted technique, the labor of application is more than with the previously mentioned foams. However, microballoons provide an extremely efficient sandwich structure with higher mechanical strengths than are possible with conventional plastic foams.

A FOAM CORE CONSTRUCTION TECHNIQUE

The proper handling and use of new raw materials is obviously important if their best characteristics are to be realized. This is especially important in the glass-plastics field where the elements provide considerable latitude in design.

Unlike wood and metals, where stock shapes and extrusions are available to the builder, fiberglass plastics require that the fabricator make a step backward in raw-material technology and learn how to handle properly special factors of chemistry and molding.

There are a significant number of foam-core fiberglass hulls in service today. Most are under 16', but a few military prototypes are in the 40' range. Many have been extremely successful. It is fair to say, however, that some have exhibited problems relating to the low order of strength available in foam cores. The orthodox foam-glass sandwich depends upon the relatively frangible cellular core to hold the tough outer skins of fiberglass in place. By proper design, the comparative weakness of the foam can be satisfactorily overcome.

A well-designed fiberglass-foam hull has many advantages, as may be demonstrated in a molded cruising sloop, the M-25, designed by George Moore, N.A. A double-wall construction for the boat was originated and worked out by Martin Weir, N.A. and plastics engineer, to eliminate the vulnerability of the foam. The outer fiberglass skins are tied together with a web of glass roving. The resultant hull shell is a series of box beam structures of much greater integrity; the foam serves only as a secondary structural support. That is, it prevents the fiberglass web from buckling.

Construction Technique

The structure can be better understood by describing the method of molding while studying the accompanying photographs which show lay-up detail. The boat was built by the Solar Boat Co., Richmond, Calif.

The unique and key feature to Weir's construction technique involves urethane foam planks wrapped with resin-impregnated

Deckhouse is conventional wood construction. Deck and hull are molded with new foam core, glass skin method.

Solar Boat Co.

fiberglass strands. The wrapping operation is carried out on a specially developed machine. The resulting planks form a core material which can be handled in a number of different ways. The planks can be applied to a fig fixture, the outer skin laid on, and then, after cure, the jig can be removed and the inner skin laminated. Or, the process can be carried out in a cavity mold in more or less conventional sequence—outer skin, planked core, inner skin. The use of a vacuum bag insures a uniform shape and finish when the latter technique is employed.

The procedure just described may sound simple, but a great deal of work was involved in refining the process. The foam wrapping machine, for instance, evolved after a great deal of development time. Spiral wrapping a few feet of plank can be done without any special device; however, to put this on a production basis and control the lay-up and proper impregnation of resin calls for a well-designed piece of machinery.

In order to fair out the glass-wrapped foam planks, Weir has added another important step to the process. This is the application of a trowelable mixture of resin and phenolic microballoons which fills in the plank seams and levels other irregularities.

Some Hull Construction Advantages

Any well designed and constructed sandwich hull will have a number of distinctive features not found in single-skin hulls. Weir and Moore determined to take maximum advantage of these favorable characteristics. The results are evident in the M-25. The boat has 1000-lb. positive buoyancy because of the foam core. This, of course, is an unusual feature in a fixed ballast hull. The insulation, sound and vibration-deadening characteristics of the foamed-core laminate are important

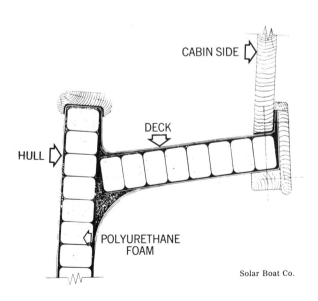

Solar Boat Co.

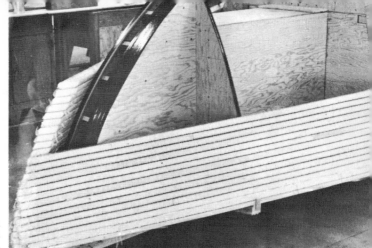

Build-up of wrapped foam cores is not unlike wooden strip planking construction.

Clamps or skewers are used to hold planks in place. Application of microballoons has been started in the transom area.

Jig has just been removed. Outer glass skin has been applied. Hull is now ready to receive inside lamination.

Photos from Solar Boat Co.

assets; and the foam core and skin laminate are fire-retardant—an important factor for prospective owners.

With the construction technique, an extremely stiff, strong, and lightweight structure is possible. The fiberglass webs joining the opposite skin laminates overcomes one of the major objections to conventional foam cores—its susceptibility to failure in shear and compression when encountering severe impact.

Perhaps one of the most interesting and important features in Mr. Weir's system concerns the initial low mold or tooling cost. It is a factor of considerable importance where only one or two hulls are to be built. His foam plank system provides a method of obtaining a hull without the usual cavity or male mold. In actual fact, the foam core serves as the mold and becomes an integral part of the hull, as may be seen from the photographs.

PENGUINS IN GLASS

Hard-chined, flat-sided hull designs have presented some special problems for fiberglass construction. While the material is much stronger and tougher than wood, its specific weight is considerably greater, and on an equal thickness basis it lacks stiffness compared to wood. In the case of relatively thin fiberglass laminates it is necessary to furnish means of preventing unwanted "oil canning" or more serious buckling deflections.

In the case of fully-shaped, round-bilge hull designs, the problem is minimized; such curves contribute natural stiffness. For example, most solid-shell fiberglass dinghies have no frames. Deflections are minimal and the small amount of elastic "give" improves impact and puncture-

The Penguin Class sailboat was designed for simple, economical development in plywood. Sandwich reinforcement is proving to be the best fiberglass construction method for hard-chined hulls.

resistance. Thus, hull form and structural design detail combine to produce adequate rigidity. But, as fiberglass has been progressively adopted by one-design classes, certain hull forms have posed demanding requirements with regard to weight-stiffness criteria.

The Penguin is a good example. This boat was designed for simple, economical construction in plywood. Furthermore, she has no real deck structure, which makes her open hull even more susceptible to torsional wracking. Well designed plywood hulls also are light, strong and stiff. A Penguin-type hull can be built up with a solid "single skin" fiberglass laminate, but keeping within the minimum weight requirement without excessive flexibility is a problem with conventional frame-stiffening techniques. It is just not as efficient as a proper choice of sandwich laminate.

"Unicore": Its Construction and Features

Unicore demonstrates some advanced structural features and undoubtedly will be more widely used as time goes on. Bill Schock of W.D. Schock Co., Cal., builder of fiberglass boats, provided an ideal solution to the previously-mentioned problems of molding the Penguin. For this boat, the minimum weight target is 137 lb. Schock maintains that using the Unicore construction technique, hulls are coming out very close to 140

1—"Unicore" fiberglass sandwich reinforcement is supplied in roll form (left). Polyurethane foam mandrels provide the separation between the glass facings. Mandrels may be stitched in place or inserted after cloth is stitched together. 2—Cross sections (right) of typical "Unicore" hull sandwich moldings show rectangular geometry. Fiberglass webs contribute great strength by tying skins together and minimizing shear and compressive loads on the relatively weak foam core.

3—Using a conventional cavity mold for hull (left), the outer skin (1 oz. mat and 7 oz. cloth) is layed up against the colored gel coat. A glass tape is being added as an extra reinforcement at the chine. Note the integral centerboard molding. 4—(Right) Pattern-cut Unicore is placed on top of the outer skin. Transverse orientation of flutes is dictated by pattern cutting. In larger, higher-stressed hulls, web or flute orientation would be extremely important to the structural efficiency required.

lb., and the boats are exceptionally rigid with a nice solid feel under sail.

Fabrication of a Unicore sandwich is basically similar to a quilting operation. Layers of glass cloth are stitched together around a mandrel system. The size and shape of the mandrels control the form and dimension of the sandwich during the molding operation. A roll of the prefabricated Unicore is shown in photograph No. 1 and cross sections of the resultant laminate can be seen in photograph No. 2.

A one-inch deep by two-inch wide rectangular Unicore configuration was selected for the Penguin hull. It can be visualized that the geometry of the webs and the dimensions of the sandwich can be varied considerably according to the form of the mandrels which are selected.

The foam inserts or mandrels are cut from a slab of 2-lb./cu. ft.-density polyurethane. The foam serves a number of useful functions. Structurally, it gives a secondary support to the fiberglass webs and increases compressive strength perpendicular to the faces. From a service

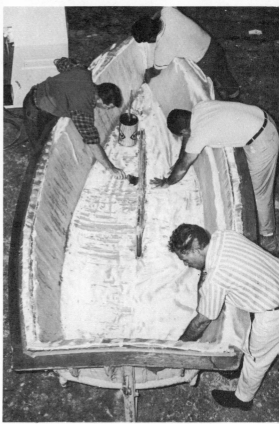

5—After the Unicore material is in place, polyester resin is carefully applied (left) so that all portions of the dry glass sandwich will be properly impregnated. Note the cutout forward of the trunk where the mast step will be mounted. 6—Once the latter process is completed, an inner, finishing layer of 7-oz. cloth is formed in place over the Unicore sandwich (right), the resin can be seen showing through the dry fabric being worked into place.

point of view, the foam sandwich provides great integral reserve buoyancy; there is no need for air tanks or styrofoam blocks. The interior of the hull is smooth and level without obstructing frames.

The fiberglass web membranes tie the outer skins together and the geometrical shape seen here creates a multiple "I" beam construction in the direction of the flutes. The integral glass webs reduce shear and compressive loads on the relatively weak foam. If the hull sandwich is punctured, the webs help to localize damage by restricting core-face delamination and shear failure of the foam in the horizontal plane.

Lay-Up System with Unicore

From a production standpoint, Unicore adapts itself rather easily to conventional boat molding techniques. The only extra process burden is the use of a vacuum bag system. It does seem to be mandatory since the core material needs some pressure for it to assume a level plane and to

53

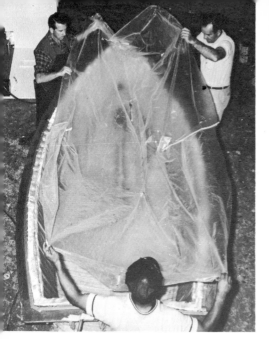

7—(Above left) Plastic vacuum bag is placed over the uncured, resin-impregnated sandwich laminate. Vacuum pump exhausts air between the bag and the laminate. Vacuum bag must be used with Unicore material in order to compress the sandwich and drive off unnecessary resin.

8 (Above right) Plastic film has been sucked down against the sandwich laminate. Workmen are smoothing the plastic film—distributing excess resin outward and upward towards the bleeder strip at the gunwale. In background are hoses and pump for air exhaust process.

9 (Left) Bow cross section of Penguin molded with Unicore sandwich. Note clear resin stripe in center which shows sandwich construction. The remainder of the interior is covered with a spackled paint that is often used on the inside of fiberglass hulls.

enable the lay-up men to work out excess resin.

The process starts with an initial outer skin applied in a fiberglass cavity mold—colored resin "gel" coat, a layer of glass reinforcing mat, a layer of glass cloth (photograph No. 3). At this point the process departs from the ordinary contact-molded, single skin system. In photograph No. 4, the pattern-cut Unicore material is being fitted in place on top of the outer skin. The next photograph (No. 5) shows application and distribution of the polyester resin. Immediately following this step, another layer of cloth is smoothed down on the saturated sandwich material (see photo

No. 6). One can note the resin striking up through the dry fabric. Before the resin-impregnated sandwich and the finishing layer of cloth have hardened, a plastic film, or what is called a "bag," is spread over the surface (photo No. 7).

The film is sealed around the edges of the mold. By means of the vacuum pump seen in the background, the air between the bag and the laminate is exhausted, thus creating an atmospheric pressure of 15 lb. per sq. in. In photograph No. 8 the workmen are smoothing out wrinkles in the film, sweeping air bubbles and excess resin outward and upward toward the peripheral bleeder strip at the gunwale.

After the resin has hardened, the vacuum is released and the film stripped away leaving a level, smooth finish. The vacuum pressure has the virtue of compressing the sandwich properly in place and allows the removal of excess resin which may occur in spongy sections of the laminate.

Any pressure system usually does permit a higher glass concentration and a corresponding increase in specific physical strength. In the fabrication of critical aircraft parts, for instance, reduction of resin content is important for it is simply excess weight. This is one of the reasons why vacuum molding is widely used in that industry.

LIGHTNING CONSTRUCTION IN GLASS

A number of years ago, officials of the Lightning Class Association started investigating fiberglass. Materials and construction methods were held as open as possible in order to encourage inventive solutions to the fundamental problems. The major challenge has been to achieve adequate panel stiffness without excess weight and of course to do this at a reasonable cost.

Technical progress was very slow in the first few years. Incentive was lacking too, because enthusiasm for fiberglass had not really caught on. In an attempt to keep some of the older hulls going, the Association approved fiberglass covering. The practice became popular to rejuvenate Lightnings which were used for daysailing, but few if any of these glass-skinned boats developed into truly "hot" racers.

Fiberglass single skin and frame techniques have been used with limited success on designs like the Lightning. Perhaps only in the case of a boat such as the Snipe, where there is a high allowable weight, can sufficient stiffness be furnished by a relatively thick single skin shell.

The Lippincott Boat Works, a top builder of Lightnings, introduced their first fiberglass models in 1964. In a short period of time these first hulls set a notable racing record. Within a year interest in their wooden hulls was virtually nonexistent.

The Lippincott people felt from the outset of their development work that some sort of a sandwich panel construction was necessary to obtain the required weight and stiffness characteristics. They were not entirely

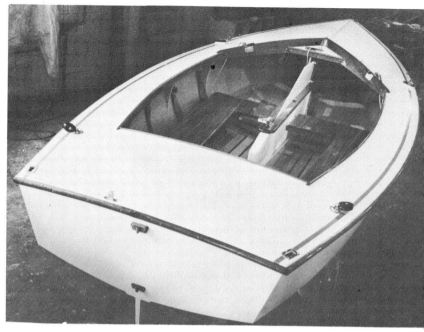

Lippincott fiberglass Lightning is hard to distinguish from th
trim provide a natural dressing appearance. The smooth, hig

satisfied with balsa core and syntactic foam core which were already being employed in some new fiberglass Lightnings. Development effort was focused on the polyurethane foams. It was discovered that the popular, light densities, two to four pounds per cubic foot, were lacking in sufficient strength. Namely, the light density foams broke down and crushed too easily under impact and flex bending. However, when the foam was densified to about eight pounds and encompassed with high tensile glass skins, the panels had great strength, stiffness and resiliency. Lippincott has not been able to buy preformed slabs of foam to his exact reinforcements and therefore finds it necessary to mold and slice his own. While this operation does not require elaborate equipment, the forming of the foam takes considerable care. The raw chemicals are expensive and waste is costly.

Lippincott Construction Procedure

As in the case of most all series production of fiberglass hulls, a cavity mold is employed for the deck and hull units. A colored "gel" coat of resin is first applied in the mold, then the outer skin of fiberglass mat and woven fabric is laid up. After cure, slabs of preformed foam are fitted into place against the skin. This requires a planned procedure of cutting,

...ooden counterpart. Mahogany floor boards, seats and
...loss hull (right) is the product of precision molds.

Left—Note deck details, molded-in anti-
skid finish. Right—Fiberglass rudder
is light, strong and requires little maintenance. Centerboard trunk (below) is
usually molded, has a stiff mounting.

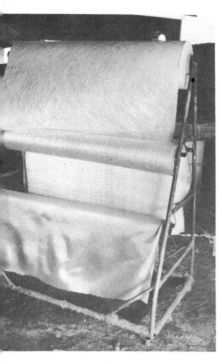

(b) In foam core, above, note the unicellular structure.

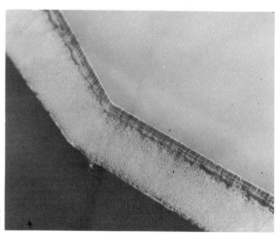

(A) Above—Fiberglass reinforcements for the "skins" are noted on the rack; top to bottom: glass mat, glass woven roving and glass cloth.

(c) Right—Note how the fiberglass laminated skins bond to the core in cross section.

fitting and tailoring the foam segments. And finally the inner skin of fiberglass is laminated over the foam. The thickness of the foam varies as to the location in the hull—about ⅝" in the bottom and ½" in the topsides and deck. The plies of glass mat and fabric vary according to the stress concentrations, being somewhat thicker in the bottom and tapering away in the sides and deck. The outer skin of glass in the hull bottom is appreciably heavier than the inner skin in order to take care of impact loads and the occasional misfortune of grounding the hull.

Because of the great stiffness and monocoque strength which is imparted by this sandwich construction, few additional frames or supporting members are required. The reader will note that there are no side frames, just a few on the bottom which serve as much as attachment

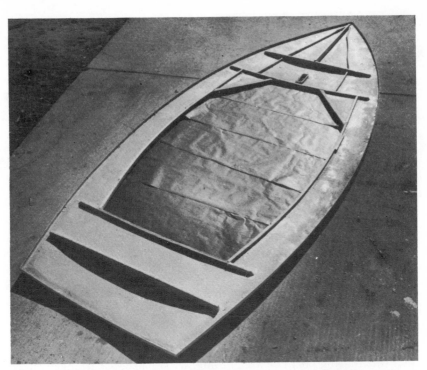

Bottom and top view of finished deck before mounting on the hull. Local wood stiffeners are required in addition to the basic foam-glass sandwich.

Hull is ready to receive deck. No side framing is necessary, only knees to support deck. Bottom transverse members make for easy attachment of floorboards. Note extension of molded trunk which serves as mast step.

for the floorboards as to provide bottom panel strength. Since there tend to be relatively high, localized deck loads imposed on the working areas of a small racing boat like a Lightning, we see a special arrangement of stiffeners that supplements the basic sandwich.

Fiberglass construction has made one very important contribution to centerboard daysailers, relative to the wooden models—no more leaky centerboard trunks or annoying leaks along the adjacent garboard area. But not all glass centerboard trunks we have seen are properly designed or built. The Lippincott model seems especially well turned out. It has an engineered look, and it is strong and stiff with a solid connection to the hull bottom.

Not all glass sailboats are equipped with a fiberglass rudder, but the Lippincotts are doing so. To design and build a good glass model at a reasonable cost is not so simple, wood is naturally adaptable to small boat rudders.

About Repairs

A well-designed and built fiberglass sandwich panel can absorb and efficiently distribute a greater amount of impact energy than a single skin laminate of the equivalent weight. A puncture or rupture of the Lippincott sandwich hull is no more difficult to repair than the more or less conventional single skin hull. The damage will be localized to the area of impact. If a section has to be replaced, a new piece of foam must be inserted and fiberglass laminated over it, blending in with the old surface. Small punctures can be filled with scrap glass and resin, or resin putty, followed by a surface patch.

A BIG CALIFORNIA CAT

The problems of molding large "one-off" fiberglass hulls seem to be yielding to ingenuity and a greater familiarity with plastic materials. **Glass Slipper**, the big California "cat" shown in the accompanying photographs, features the use of very economical plywood veneer molds and an efficiently developed foam sandwich core.

So many one-of-a-kind glass hulls have now been built using the wooden male plug approach that this system can now be said to be a preferred or standard method for achieving a single yacht hull. A more recent development, however, is the use of foam core sandwich construction in larger size hulls. Synthetic foam chemistry has advanced considerably to make this possible: costs have been reduced, density and consistency are more controllable—application techniques have achieved greater refinement and efficiency.

Before entering a detailed discussion of the molded fiberglass hulls it is first worthwhile to describe some of the interesting construction features and the general dimensions of the **Glass Slipper**.

This California-built cat is 50′ l.o.a., 20′ beam and displaces 16,000 ᶫb.

1—White "gel coat" of resin is applied to plywood hull mold (left) with spray gun. Note bands of veneer running vertically. 2—Right, the first layer of 20-oz. glass cloth is receiving a Glas-Craft spray gun application of catalyzed resin.

Only the hull shells are of plastic construction. Large aircraft type box beam members, fabricated with spruce and plywood facings, tie the two hulls rigidly together. These primary members drop down into the hulls so that loads are distributed over a generous area. There are five plywood bulkheads in each hull. The decks, wing foil section and superstructure are plywood and ribbon grain mahogany. To complement the low maintenance feature of the glass hulls, all exterior surfaces are covered with fiberglass cloth and polyester resin. Mahogany brightwork on the cabin trunk is fiberglassed with clear resin to allow the natural, rich grain to show through. California fiberglass technicians seem to be particularly skilled at clear fiberglass applications. Built up wooden sheer clamps are locked into the sandwich hull laminate to provide strength, rigidity and a solid fastening member for the deck. Laminated cedar keels in the hulls are reinforcement in case of grounding.

The foam fiberglass sandwich laminate design in the hulls is especially interesting. A significant number of larger boats have been built in recent years using various types of foam cores. Materials and methods are being improved. The advantages are attractive and significant—good local and overall hull rigidity with a minimum of obstructing frames, weight savings, high potential for reserve buoyancy. Sound deadening and insulating values are perhaps of lesser importance, but useful assets.

3—Four-pound density polyurethane foam is sprayed (left) on the inner fiberglass skin to a depth of approximately 2-1/2". 4—Right hull mold has been completely encased in foam, left mold is bare. Note port light cut-out inserts.

A key element in the proper structural design of the foam glass sandwich was the selection of foam thickness and density. Using special test equipment a final materials combination was determined. From previous catamaran design experience three-eighths inch fir plywood had proven satisfactory for hull shells of a similar size. This plus other appropriate scantling data furnished the basis for qualifying the glass-plastics sandwich. The plastics combination finally selected was able to support a maximum point loading of 440 lb. on a nine inch by two inch specimen—equivalent to the capability of three-quarter inch fir plywood. The foamed core laminate consists of the following: inner skin, two plies of 20 oz. glass cloth; core, two-inch, four-pound density polyurethane foam; outer skin, two plies of 20 oz. glass cloth and two plies of 1½ oz. glass mat. Resultant skin thicknesses are approximately 1/8" inside and 3/16" outside.

Special consideration was given to the density of the foam required. Panels with two, four, six and eight pound per cubic foot densities were tested. It might be presumed that a six or eight pound foam would be more desirable from a strength standpoint. However, Glas-Craft engineers found that in consideration of panel design, anticipated loading and service conditions, all were satisfied by four pound density.

The rather simple shape of the cat hulls was of help in the development of the molds. They were built in four days at a total cost of

5—Guided by specially designed leveling rails, a workman (left) planes the foam down to an exact depth of two inches. 6—Right—The exterior laminate consists of two layers of 1-1/2-oz. mat and one layer of 20-oz. glass cloth.

$1,350. We are impressed by this very modest investment and it is convincing evidence that mold or tooling costs need not be an excessive cost burden on large "one-off" glass hull projects. The mold construction was very light. Narrow panels of 1/8" Japanese plywood were formed over set up stations. By fastening the plywood with a staple gun and employing masking tape to bridge any gaps and discrepancies, the job went very rapidly. Since the sandwich laminate was molded over the exterior of these plugs, their dimensions were proportioned exactly 2-2/8" less than the outside measurements of the actual hulls. The plywood mold surfaces were then treated with a sealer and a plastic film release agent.

As a first step in the laminating procedure, a white gel coat of resin was sprayed onto the hull molds (photo 1). Since Glas-Craft are primarily designers and fabricators of all types of plastic spray gun equipment, they naturally used their apparatus in many phases of construction. Resin deposition by gun is much faster and more efficient on large area moldings than using a brush or roller. The Glas-Craft gun can put out as much as 12 lb. of catalyzed resin per minute.

Two layers of 20 oz. glass cloth were then laminated in place to form the inner skin (photo 2). After cure, polyurethane foam was sprayed on to a depth of approximately 2½". A rough control check of thickness was provided by periodically punching the foam build up with an ice pick

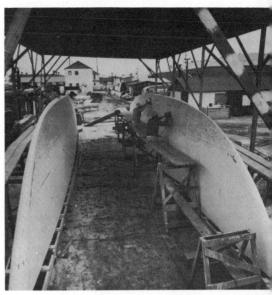

7—A final fill coat of white polyester resin is applied. All resin and foam plastics were sprayed on with the gun depositors. 8—Small discrepancies were faired with orbital sanders and touched up with resin (right).

probe. In all, 700 lb. of foam, applied at a rate of nine pounds per minute, were used to construct the two hulls. The gun depositer can be seen operating in photo No. 3.

In order to obtain an exact foam core depth of two inches, a special planing system was devised. A guide assembly incorporating eight-foot long flexible rails and three-inch perpendicular spikes allowed accurate contour routing of the irregular foam surface. The spikes were inserted into the foam until they contacted the fiberglass laminate beneath. This planing operation took two men two days to complete. The router can be seen in photo 5.

The remaining laminating operations were quite straightforward. Two layers of 20 oz. cloth and two layers of 1½ oz. mat were applied over the leveled foam surface to provide the outside skin.

There are quite a number of interesting features to the yacht which are worth pointing out. There is enough polyurethane foam in the sandwich hulls of **Glass Slipper** to make the catamaran completely unsinkable, and to give her a remarkable amount of reserve buoyancy. Even if both hulls were completely flooded, they would submerge no more than about 30". A new, antifouling polyester resin coat was applied to the hull bottoms to discourage marine growth. This is a bottom treatment developed by Ram Chemical Co. of Gardena, Cal. **Glass Slipper** carries a 120 hp. inboard-outboard auxiliary power plant. The outdrive retracts when not in use. The power plant cooling system was re-designed so that the engine can be run with the outdrive out of water to utilize its two alternators for recharging the ship's batteries.

Accommodations appear very commodious. Each hull contains a master stateroom with a king size double bed, a head with shower, and two single berths for crew members. The wing section is 13' x 14', with 6'4" headroom, and contains galley, dining area and chart table. On her initial sea trials the boat achieved speeds to 16 knots under power. The boat is steered by twin rudders through a two wheel system. Each wheel controls both rudders, but should damage occur, each wheel and rudder may be made independent of the other simply by pulling a locking pin.

It is quite obvious that fiberglass boats in the future will exhibit a combination of single-skin and sandwich construction, each technique being used where it does its best job. Out of the research work which is going on continuously will evolve a range of core materials to fit various needs. The plastic engineer and boatbuilder will be able to select those core materials that really complement the durable, tough skins which surround them.

The continuing challenge is to find core materials which are low in cost, easy to work with, and have physical properties that measure up to the tough fiberglass skins.

If the reader is left with the impression that the presently available core materials leave something to be desired, this is an opinion also shared by the writer. We feel that good structures are being developed with what is offered to the builder today, but that the materials must be accepted with some compromise. The combined requirements of suitable strength, acceptable cost and favorable adaptability are not completely met by the materials we have discussed.

CHAPTER 5

Wood—Fiberglass Composite

SHEATHING OF WOODEN HULLS and decks has been practiced for a good many years; this use of fiberglass is older than the molded boat. In fact, the widest use of fiberglass materials in the early years was in the covering application. For example, at that time strip-planked outboards were popular. As outboard motors moved up in horsepower, the resultant speeds and strains to which these strip boats were subject were severe, and they loosened up and leaked. Some manufacturers turned to fiberglass covering to increase strength and tightness of the boats. Experience gained with the basic materials in covering persuaded many of these builders that the all-molded boat had more advantages, and so they made the transition.

Glass-resin materials have been successfully used over wood for local repairs, waterproofing, worm protection and structural strength. Many of the features of a molded glass hull can be imparted to a wooden hull by this protective sheathing. Nevertheless, one cannot equate the molded and the covered hull except perhaps on an individual basis.

The idea of combining wood and fiberglass is still not popular with many boatmen. Possibly, this stems from disappointing personal experience or familiarity with some failures. Fiberglass covering has not been successful in all cases, and there are at least two good reasons for

Plywood hull shell of popular Newporter design receiving fiberglass cloth and resin. Many composite features are demonstrated in this boat. Tanks and cockpit are solid molded units. All exposed wood sections are sheathed in fiberglass.

Newport Fiberglass Boats

Mahogany veneer strips
were stapled to ribbands on
"Arpege" mold.

Jean Filloux

this. In some instances it has been thought of as a cure-all. Secondly, the variety of conditions that may be encountered sometimes requires experienced judgment and technique to complete the covering job properly.

The majority of boat owners who have fiberglass hulls or decks have been satisfied with the results. As long as wooden craft are built, fiberglassing or some similar protective covering system will be popular.

Monocoque Wood and Fiberglass Hulls

It is only one logical step further to consider adding a heavy buildup of glass over a wooden form to achieve a structural fiberglass shell. This technique has been successfully used on old and new construction. For example, an old derelict 36' lobster boat was restored and returned to service after receiving 3/16th lamination of fiberglass. It was only necessary to replace a few of the deteriorated primary framing members because the tough skin of glass restored the overall strength integrity of the hull. The story of the boat's rebirth is told at the end of this chapter.

As to integral wooden molds for new construction, we know of a number of successful projects. Illustration of the 42' ketch **Arpege** demonstrates the use of a wood/glass combination. In this particular case the wood veneer shell approximately matched the thickness of the fiberglass overlay. The monocoque hull shell was about three-quarters of an inch thick—three-eighths mahogany veneer, three-eighths fiberglass. **Arpege** was a relatively early experiment using this technique, built at the end of 1955. Later examples have had thinner wood shells.

MERITS OF COMBINING WOOD AND FIBERGLASS

Debate has persisted over the years among boat designers and builders about the merits of combining wood and fiberglass. The debate has also included the use of metals. Some authorities have claimed that the properly built fiberglass craft should not incorporate any dissimilar materials in its structure, as the materials are incompatible and set up undesirable stresses. But well-designed wood/glass combinations are proving to give little of the trouble that many anticipated.

Broadly speaking, then, since no engineering approach can be perfect, a composite construction can be considered successful if it solves more problems than it introduces. Few structures, whether a building, a vehicle, or an industrial machine, represent a combination of perfectly homogenous parts. It is more a matter of how the different materials in such structures are assembled so that the effect of their physical differences is minimized.

To summarize: the glass-covered wooden boat and the molded type are fundamentally different in that one makes use of the material as protective envelope and the other, with a really heavy skin, counts on the glass and resin combination for true structural value. However, for practical reasons of economy and simplicity of engineering, we do find combinations of varying types which make the two concepts closely related.

Differential Expansion and Modulus

Shop talk on this subject invariably brings up two specific questions on wood/glass combinations as pertinent points of discussion, relating to covered and molded boats which incorporate wood in some way.

One contention is that, because wood will come and go considerably with varying moisture content, it will break away from the reinforced plastic bonded to it. Glass-plastic material has a very low coefficient of elongation. In truth, these stresses are set up, but by proper design or application they may be accommodated. For instance, in covering a wooden boat with glass successfully you must restrain the expansion and contraction forces. The solution varies with the type of construction. A wide, heavy-planked hull must receive at least two or three layers of glass cloth. Plywood, on the other hand, is relatively stable. One layer is usually sufficient, except at the joints. The nature of the wood must be considered relative to proper adhesion. Hard, close-grained woods, particularly oak, are difficult to bond to properly with polyester resin.

The molded boat which incorporates wood for some structural purposes is relatively free of the above complexities, but adjustments must be made so that the two materials work with each other instead of in conflict. An example of poor design would be a stiff, hard-wood stringer used to support a relatively flexible glass hull shell. In operation, the hull will pant or flex, perhaps causing a critical stress point at the junction with the more rigid wood member. The solution can be worked out in a number of ways, one being to stiffen the unsupported panel sufficiently so that the "hard spot" is not created.

Do Glass/Wood Combinations Cause Rot?

Experience and physical testing strongly indicate that neither glass covering nor glass encapsulation of wood promotes rot. If a rot condition was prevalent or latent at the time of glassing, the covering will probably not inhibit the extension of the condition. But lab tests conducted by a research firm, Forest Products, show that the resin has a most poisonous effect on rot spores. As stated before, just whether the laminating resins can be classified as suitable fungicide treatment is not known at this time. It has been observed, however, that double-bottom chambers containing wood members in a dead air space don't appear to show wood decay, and it can be assumed that the toxic effect of the resin in this confined area acts as a deterrent.

The glass covering or sheathing is similar to a paint film or a canvas covering, and does not in itself start a rot condition. Indeed, since the glass is more impervious to moisture than paint or canvas, it provides an even greater protection against decay. The problem is generally confined to observing good wooden boat-building practices, if and when wood is to be combined with glass.

RESURRECTION WITH FIBERGLASS

This story concerns a resurrection of a 40-year old lobster boat that had been retired to crumble away on the beach in Thomaston, Me. The derelict was given a new lease on life by an energetic and imaginative plastics engineer named Jan S. Irvine. The saga of her rebuilding was related by Mr. Irvine in the October, 1961, issue of "The National Fisherman," whose editor we wish to thank for loaning us the accompanying photographs.

The reader may be curious why such an ambitious rebuilding project was undertaken. The back waters of coastal areas are littered with worn-out hulks that are of little salvage value, much less worthy of returning to the sea. The answer to the question is to be found in the man and his vigorous belief that many aged wooden hulls can economically be put back in service by laminating a structural shell of glass around the old

Forty year old retired lobster boat as she lay on the shores of Thomaston, Me.

The National Fisherman

bones of any vessel which is acceptably true in form. Jan, therefore, went in search of a suitable derelict to prove his point. He found his subject, a 34′ hull, on the shore in Thomaston. The boat was in sad condition. Moss and grass flourished here and there in her rotted seams, and the deckhouse was out of shape and collapsing. Important to Jan was that the backbone of the hull was firm and true, her sheer was not hogged, and the hull, although weak and riddled with rot, provided a fair enough mold form on which to laminate a new glass shell.

While frames, planking, and fastenings had deteriorated, the main structural elements were still sound, and his educated eye told him that a properly applied glass envelope would knit the entire hull back together again. Jan has fiberglassed over 60 wooden hulls in the course of his career, and he knew from experience how much material would be needed and just the right technique to get the maximum benefit from the glass plastic sheathing.

The Procedure

The hulk was removed from the harbor bank to a boat shed for the reconstruction work. She was first stripped down to the bare shell. The trunk and standing top were torn off and discarded, the flooring and much of the ceiling were removed and scrapped. The old paint on the hull was burned off with a blow torch in order to hasten drying of the wood planking. Removing paint with a torch preparatory to fiberglassing is generally not an approved practice, for paint oils may be driven into the wood and can inhibit the subsequent resin bond. However, in this case, the heavy paint film was old and dried out, and stripping with an electric sander was a tedious alternative.

The drying -out process took weeks, with only local and somewhat ineffective space heat available. It was decided that the covering would be applied to the hull as it lay in an upright position, but facilitated somewhat by canting her from one bilge to the other as the job proceeded. Stripping the hull resulted in some distortion, but was corrected by proper placement of interior props.

The first step in reconstruction was to dig out and fill rotted plank sections. Broken and deteriorated frames were ignored, as it was felt that the heavy glass skin more than replaced their strength value. Irvine elected to use two material systems to fill the rotted areas. For big holes he mixed a viscous compound of scrap fiberglass and resin, which provided an enormously strong patch filler. For small seam gaps and minor holes he used a polyester putty compound that trowels in place much like a standard wood dough filler, but is much stronger. Because of the condition of the hull, a good many hours were spent on this particular operation.

When the filled areas were sanded fair, the hull was ready to receive its sheathing of fiberglass. The job called for a heavy buildup of fiberglass. Jan therefore settled on three layers of woven-roving cloth. The material selected weighed about 24-ounces per square yard—two and a half times the weight of standard boat-covering cloth. The resultant skin, including a finishing layer of boat cloth, provided a glass-plastic skin thickness of about 5/32" to 3/16".

As can be seen from the photograph, the fabric was applied vertically to the hull. The panels were butted and the butted seams in subsequent layers staggered by four or more inches to preserve the strength continuity of the envelope. Because of the dry, porous nature of the wood, two prime coats of polyester resin were applied. The fabric was pressed down into the tacky resin and held itself in place properly except in the vicinity of the bilges where the weight of the cloth tended to make the material pull away. For these areas and on the oak keel, Jan used a viscous epoxy trowel paste which held the heavy material properly during the curing.

Fore, aft and side-deck areas were also fiberglassed. The material was carried over the sheer and down the topsides; in this manner considerable additional stiffness and strength was provided to this critical area of the old hull.

After the third layer of woven roving was applied and impregnated with resin, a finishing layer of boat cloth was laid on. Because of the coarse nature of woven roving, the finer weave of the boat cloth assisted in giving an even but not exactly smooth surface. The final operation involved a coat of white epoxy paint. Clear resin had been used throughout the laminating procedure, although white pigmentation of the resin could have been used in the final coats.

Panels of fiberglass fabric were butted together. This is the first layer in process. Note the resin-saturated wood to the left.

The National Fisherman

Evaluation

Before the new superstructure, internal members and machinery were installed, Mr. Irvine decided to demonstrate the ruggedness of his reconstructed hull. The bare shell was put afloat and anchored out on a rocky tidal area in the Thomaston harbor. The hull remained there for 60 tide changes, absorbing a great deal of abuse from the sharp rocks. The resultant damage was very superficial, and the local fishermen were suitably impressed with the capabilities of the fiberglass protective shell. The hull was then returned to the yard for fitting out, and she is now in daily service under the command of a local lobsterman.

In summary of this case history, one logically asks, what was proven by this project? The economics of such reconstruction are all-important. Was it less expensive to repair the old hull than to build a new one? Mr. Irvine states that a new comparable hull, less power, would have cost about $5,000. He bought the derelict for $50 and spent about $4,000 in materials and labor to put the boat in "like-new" condition.

Mr. Irvine has presented a most persuasive and concrete argument for the use of fiberglass in reconstructing old hulls. The project was completely successful. It is certainly true that refinements and efficiencies can be developed in the technique and, most important, the end result is a glass-covered hull which has many advantages over its original wooden counterpart.

CHAPTER 6

Modifications and Attachments

THERE ARE THREE FUNDAMENTAL operations used in making alterations or in attaching components to a fiberglass boat. Basically, these are drilling, cutting, and bonding. A fiberglass laminate machines like a soft metal. It can be drilled easily with metal-cutting twist drills. Panels can be cut rapidly with fine-toothed metal-cutting saw blades. And, because the glass laminate yields readily to abrasive action, it is easy to work with files and sandpaper. In general, hard-surfaced metal-cutting saw blades, bits and files are recommended. The glass fiber will dull almost any cutting instrument after repeated use.

Understand Construction Details of the Boat

In order to make secure and dependable connections and fastenings, it is important to know how the particular boat is constructed. For instance, many auxiliary sailboats have sandwich core decks which may employ balsa wood or various foam materials between the fiberglass surfaces. Soft-core materials like this have poor screw-holding power, so a back-up system is necessary. If however, plywood sections are used to stiffen the deck, fittings can be fastened directly to the glass-plywood combination. Most interior partitions and bulkheads are of plywood construction. Fastening to these members requires conventional techniques. However, when considering a connection to the hull or deck shell, examine and determine the type of thickness of the fiberglass laminate so that the most suitable bonding or fastening method will be used.

Bonded Installations

Except for the mounting of hardware and trim, resinglass bonds are as basic to a fiberglass hull as screw fasteners and glue are to a wooden craft. Resin-bonded glass comprises the basic laminate. Strips of resin-impregnated glass are used to make hull-to-deck joints, secure plywood bulkheading, bond stiffening members in place and many other applications. The system is similar in a way to welding a metal structure. The resultant bond is both chemical and mechanical in nature. While the resin is readily distinguishable as the bonding agent, important strength and stability are imparted by the glass fibers.

Fiberglass boats in various stages of completion at the Pearson Corp.

Most all bonded connections made at the factory during the production of the boat are made with polyester resin, the same as used in the basic laminate. But this is accomplished under shop conditions and with experienced workmen. The average boat owner will find, however, that the superior adhesion of epoxy cement insures best results.

It will be helpful to understand bonding techniques if any extensive modifications are to be carried out on the inside of a fiberglass hull. The owner may want to install a shelf, seat or locker against the hull. Screwing or bolting directly into the hull shell is generally not practical. The new unit must be bonded in place.

This can be done by fiberglassing the finished piece to the hull laminate with strips of glass and resin, or wooden cleats can be fiberglassed in place and the cabinet work screw fastened to the wooden blocks. To make a good fiberglass bonded connection only a few requirements have to be carefully observed. Fiberglass-bonded connections are not hard to do, but care is required to obtain maximum strength and dependability.

First of all the sections to be joined, whether they be wood or glass, must be rough sanded, clean and dry. It is also important to note that many fiberglass boats are finished off on the inside with various types of decorative paints. It is necessary to sand away this paint film so that the bond is made to the laminate, not to the paint. Use a four or six-inch glass tape as the primary bond reinforcement. Provide sufficient overlap. Two to three inches is adequate for all but the most highly stressed joints. Two layers of tape on either side of the wooden member will make a good, strong connection. If very heavy loads are to be carried, such as an engine mount or a lift pad, use alternate layers of mat and tape fabric to obtain thickness and rigidity. Sufficient layers of glass must be built up to prevent any peeling action.

Epoxy cements are appropriate and useful for mounting miscellaneous fixtures on the inside of glass hulls and in making "spot weld" connections or repairs. For instance, a hanger for a boat hook or port light curtains can be installed by first cementing a block of wood to the fiberglass surface and then screw-fastening the metal hardware to the wooden member. Epoxy is particularly recommended when bonding to metal.

All photos by Rosenfeld

Left—Making bolt holes for mounting sheet winch on molded fiberglass pedestal. The same precision required as when fastening to metal surfaces. Right—High-speed twist drills cut through fiberglass laminate as it it were soft metal. Bolt should fit snugly to prevent working.

Left—Cleat assembly ready for installation showing flexible sealant on the bolt shanks and scrap glass laminate to act as load distributing plate beneath deck. Right—Nicely finished mahogany block used as back-up mounting for sheet winch or mooring cleat.

 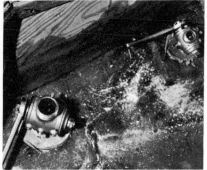

Left—Proper installation of seacock is important. Prestite sealant is carefully applied to flange. Watertightness must be achieved with sealing compound. Right—Seacock assembly with its piping connections may be subject to working. As a rule laminate thickness must be locally increased in way of fixture.

Bow mooring chock shown installed before deck is joined to hull. Here again scrap glass laminate acts as washer and strengthening agent. Right—To facilitate production Pearson mounts all standard hardware before major components are assembled. Note joining of deck (top) and hull flanges.

 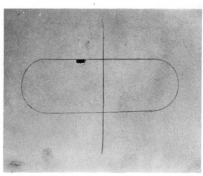

Pearson fastens hull to deck with rivets. Strip of sealant makes joint watertight. Rubber chafe strip will be snapped over flange joint. Right—Portlight pattern is traced out with template on cabin trunk of a Triton auxiliary. Pilot hole is drilled to start saw cut.

Such items as cleats and chocks should be bolted in place. Use a twist drill close to the size of the bolt to prevent possible working and enlargement of the hole. An electric power drill is much easier than a hand-operated type. Always use generous-sized washers between the fiberglass and the nut. Lock washers are recommended when any sustained vibration is involved.

If the laminate is thin and unusually great loads are expected, as in the case of a mooring or towing cleat, bolt or fasten through into a wooden plate which will distribute stresses over a greater area. Factory-installed chainplates, stemplates, towing eyes, etc., are generally bolted into a "beefed up" laminate section, but the owner usually does not have to go to this trouble. On larger boats, such as auxiliaries and inboard power craft, a tight, leaf-proof fit of such hardware is important. Use a flexible sealing compound or rubber type gasket.

Left—Powered saber saw readily cuts through 3/16" laminate. Metal cutting key hole saw can be used in absence of power equipment. Right—Portlight cut out complete. Metal flange will conceal rough edges, but they can be ground smooth with fine file or sand paper.

Left—An outboard bracket for an Electra day sailer. When through-bolting to transom the use of sealant and backing blocks is essential. Right—Pearson provides for easy conversion of a day sailer to inboard auxiliary power with knock-out blank (white) in rudder and deadwood.

Left—Conversion completed. The specific area in deadwood is a thin, hollow laminate. The rudder is of wood. Right—Inside lead ballast being lowered into a new Triton. The old model mounted outside ballast.

Left—Ballast in position to test fit. Lead will be grouted in place with gasket of resin-saturated fiberglass mat. Right—Ballast sealed over with fiberglass. System provides underbody structure of great strength, as those who have grounded such boats will testify.

The next three picture sequence shows the fabrication of a shaft log tube. Left—the resin saturated glass is spun on a metal spindle. Right—Rough buildup of glass reinforced plastic has now been completed. After allowing time for cure, surface will be machined smooth on spindle.

Use of Screw Fasteners

Because of the hard, non-compressible nature of a fiberglass laminate, wood-type screws cannot be installed properly. For the same reasons, driving a nail is a hopeless proposition.

However, special types of screws can be used. While bolting is generally preferred, there are instances when a nut and washer cannot be applied. In these cases, machine and self-tapping screws (thread forming or thread cutting) will work satisfactorily. As a rule, such fasteners are employed where mild horizontal loads are involved—small chocks, tracks, metal coaming strip, etc. In any case, the installation should be made with care.

As another rule-of-thumb, don't try to tap into a laminate that is, say, less than 5/32" thick; the screw needs sufficient thickness penetration for dependable holding power. Select a pilot drill the exact size of the screw

Left—The shaft log tube has been knocked free from metal mandrel and cut on a slant preparatory to mounting in hull. Right—Engine mounts on Pearson powerboat. Metal mount is lagged through fiberglass hat-shaped stringer into section of oak.

Left—Molded fiberglass engine mount in a Triton auxiliary. Right—Mahogany-faced plywood bulkhead before bonding to hull shell. Face is rabbeted along edges to receive bonding of fiberglass and resin.

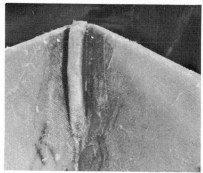

Left—Plywood floor, shelf and bulkhead panels in forepeak of power boat. All panels are fiberglassed to hull shell and are ready for painting. Right—Fiberglass inside stem reinforcement locally strengthens section where stemhead fitting will be fastened. System is used for attaching chainplate.

Left—Inside, after section of 28-foot powerboat. Note longitudinal stringers, outboard cradle mounts for gas tank (top); shelf for cockpit floor. Right—Engine installation in a 27-foot power cruiser. Note molded gutter around lip of hatch. Plywood bulkhead simplifies attachment of component.

Left—Molded fiberglass sink mounts neatly in galley section of power-boat. Unit is screw-fastened to plywood paneling. Right—Some typical fasteners: wood screws, male-female connector for grab rail, pop rivet for trim, machine screw, rivet for deck-hull connection.

barrel and then carefully turn the fastener home. Such screws will "self tap" themselves pretty well in the material, although the preparatory tapping procedure used in metals is better.

For those who wish to go further into the subject of screw-fastener installation and bonded connections, we suggest Chapter 3, "Design Details," In "Marine Design Manual for Fiberglass Reinforced Plastics," written by Gibbs & Cox and published by McGraw-Hill.

Accompanying herewith is a sequence of photographs concerning some important design details in fiberglass boat construction. The selection, while not all-inclusive, was chosen because of its usefulness to the boat owner in terms of making modifications and attachments, and as a general aid towards greater understanding of important joints and connections.

The photographs were taken in the plant of the Pearson Corp., at Bristol, R. I. While there will naturally be some variations between their techniques and those in other plants, the basic methods are generally representative of accepted practices.

Making Simple Attachments

It would be well here to cover the basic principles of how to make simple attachments to a fiberglass hull interior. Since adhesive bonding is unique and often a recommended procedure, several sketches on this method are included.   It will be very helpful to the owner if he will familiarize himself with the way his boat is put together so that the best method of mounting can be selected. He should have a rough idea of the laminate thicknesses in the hull, deck and other components. Perhaps most important, an understanding must be gained as to where sandwich panels are used and their approximate dimensions. Builders often use wood or foam plastic cores in flat sections such as the deck or cabin top. Information of this sort can generally be obtained from the dealer or certainly from the builder.

Can Mechanical Fasteners be Used?

Self-tapping screws or bolts of various types will work satisfactorily in a fiberglass laminate. They had best not be used for heavy loads unless there is sufficient thickness of material for the threads to bear upon—an eighth inch laminate, for instance, is probably the least thickness for any type of installation. Self-tapping machine bolts or screws are often used on small craft where a "blind" fastening installation is involved and the loads are relatively light. It is only necessary to drill a pilot hole and drive the fastener firmly home.

Corrosion-resistant sheet metal screws are used from time to time with the fiberglass laminates. These common fasteners typically have coarse threads on a tapered shank which will pull up properly on panels that are an eighth of an inch or less. However, they simply are not dependable enough for heavy loads. They can be considered for mounting light objects on interior facing panels.

Pop rivets are used extensively in the production of fiberglass hulls. They can be installed rapidly and are ideal for blind fastening. Metal trim for the edges of panels on deck to hull joints are often applied with pop rivets. Inexpensive pop rivet guns are now available through hardware stores. They are a very useful tool, and with some familiarity the appropriate applications on a fiberglass boat will become readily apparent.

Considering all the mechanical fastening techniques, through bolts with nuts and washers have by far the best strength and load distributing characteristics. For the mounting of deck hardware such as cleats, chocks, bits, etc., bolts are the best. Always use flat washers under the nuts and consider a wooden cleat between the laminate and the nut if the strains are severe such as in the case of a mooring cleat.

A fiberglass laminate can be worked with any hard, abrasive tool. It can be cut, machined and drilled with metal-working tools. Metal type twist drills should always be used to install fastenings.

Fastening to Cored Panels

As previously indicated, many fiberglass hulls employ foamed plastic balsa wood or plywood core construction in their decks and occasionally in the hulls. If mechanical fasteners are to be driven into these cores it is important to understand just what material is sandwiched between the fiberglass skins. If plywood is involved, this relatively dense wood will have good screw-holding characteristics. If, however, balsa wood or plastic foam is employed, these materials are too soft and through bolts are the only answer. In any case, examine the structure to determine the nature of the core material and its thickness.

Bonded Connections

Very often it is simply not practical to use metal fasteners for making attachments to fiberglass. This is particularly true if one wishes to mount an object on the inside of the hull shell. The skin is generally quite thin and it is not acceptable to bolt through the laminate. The only alternative is to bond the apparatus or assembly in place.

The proper procedure for bonded installations can be broken down into two categories—those which involve light loads and those which involve heavy loads.

Light objects like a curtain rod fixture or a boat hook shelf bracket can be screwed to a wooden cleat or block which is cemented to the hull shell. The operation merely involves these steps: first provide a neatly proportioned block of mahogany or other good quality wood which will accept the screw-fastened fitting. Several square inches of bonding surface will be sufficient. The next step is to thoroughly sand the surface of the hull where the block will make contact. You should sand away any paint that exists so that the bond is made to the laminate, not to the paint. For a neat glue joint on a smooth "gel" coat surface, it is desirable to mark the area off with tape. This prevents messy scratches from extending beyond the joint and excess cement from running down the surface. Use epoxy

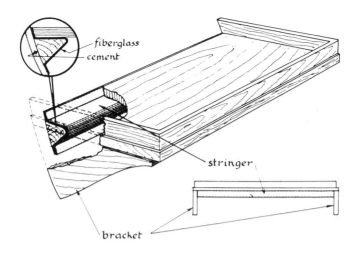

A shelf installation. Wood support is fiberglassed to hull. Shelf panel
is then screw fastened to bonded wood member.

cement to bond the block to prepared spot on the hull. Epoxy glues or
cements are commonly available from hardware stores. The material
comes in tubes or cans. You mix equal parts together, apply to both
surfaces and let cure for a day or so. You do not need pressure to obtain a
strong epoxy bond. This is one of the features of this modern adhesive.
You will probably need to hold the block in place on a vertical surface
with pressure sensitive tape.

Where heavy loads are to be carried on a mounting or where a
relatively light mounted object is subject to shock or "G" forces, the
cemented wooden block must be solidly fiberglassed to the hull. The
accompanying sketch of the anchor bracket is a good example. Another

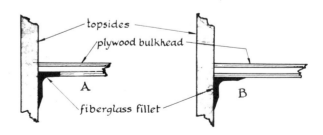

Fiberglassing of plywood bulkhead to fiberglass hull shell. Type A is
a recessed fillet. For more strength, fillet should be added to opposite side.

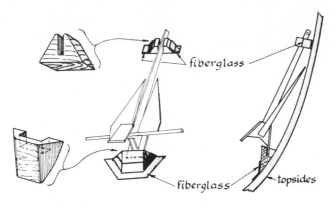

fiberglass

fiberglass

topsides

Possible anchor mount for interior stowage. Wood blocks are epoxy
bonded and fiberglassed to hull.

typical, heavy anchor bracket object would be a fire extinguisher. The
fiberglass should be laminated over the wood and overlapped several
inches onto the hull shell. Polyester resin and glass cloth or tape will do a
good job.

Two other illustrations accompanying this article demonstrate
principle to follow. The shelf installation, for instance, could be the basic
approach for developing a bunk. In the case of such a bigger assembly,
the wood brackets should also be fiberglassed to the hull. The bulkhead
joints are shown as a common type of installation. In sketch A we
indicate how a neat, flush joint can be made on a dressy plywood panel
by rabbeting the wood before fiberglassing. For any big bulkhead or one
which is stressed to any degree, apply fiberglass fillets to both sides.

The fiberglass bonds indicated are simple to carry out. If there is any
doubt about the strength or uncertainty as to procedure, make some
simple tests with scrap pieces of wood. In review the principles are as
follows:

—Prepare the surface by rough sanding. It should be clean and dry.

—Use fiberglass tape or cloth and polyester resin for laminating the
wood bulkhead to the fiberglass hull as shown in sketch No. 2.

—Overlaps of about two inches are sufficient in most instances.

—Add additional plies of glass to increase stiffness and strength as
might be required in a bulkhead fillet.

CHAPTER 7

Deck Surfaces

SECURITY UNDER FOOT IS very important to comfort and safety in a boat. The thoughtful designer or builder appreciates this and endeavors to provide a safe surface on all working areas. Hence, a discussion of fiberglass deck treatments should be helpful.

The subject breaks down into two categories—the anti-skid pattern, developed from a conventional cavity mold, and the floor or deck surface provided on wood or metal by an overlay of glass cloth and resin.

Comparisons Difficult

The optimum deck surface must have four features: maximum traction; neat, attractive appearance; durability; and ease of cleaning. It is difficult to combine all these characteristics because an improvement in one usually means a sacrifice in the other. Standards of acceptance, when comparing the old with the new, involve an appraisal of traditional materials used for working-deck areas. Canvas, wood and steel are the basic materials, but more often than not protective paints and anti-skid additives furnish the actual contact surface. Perhaps only in the case of teak or other suitable woods is the base material serving in its natural state.

The Molded Pattern

Because the "molded-in" anti-skid pattern on fiberglass boats is widely used, we hear a lot of discussion about its merits and disadvantages. In the writer's opinion the average "molded-in" pattern does not have the positive grip provided by other treatments, but it has much to recommend it over traditional surfaces. Well-designed and properly molded, it has a high degree of acceptance. The pattern can be very handsome, setting off the covering board areas, outlining a simulated king plank and, in general, introducing texture and style to an otherwise smooth, unrelieved molding.

Durability of the molded pattern is good, and with reasonable care it should give long service. The first such deck surfaces were introduced about 1955 or 1956. We have seen some of these early decks recently, and while there were imperfections due to poor molding, the anti-skid pattern has not worn down significantly. The hardness of the resin surface appears to be quite adequate considering the fact that rubber soles are usually worn on board a boat.

Because one does not expect to repaint or otherwise recondition a fiberglass deck every year, the surface must be easy to clean. Some of the first patterns trapped dirt very readily. Others did not lend well to molding, and incurred minute voids which filled with residue and were unsightly. Even a stiff bristled brush with scouring powder may not get out all the small particles.

Molding Techniques

The anti-skid pattern on fiberglass decks is usually made in the mold. When the pattern is a raised one, it has been produced by a pattern cast in the cavity and transferred from the male plug. If it is recessed on the deck it is usually a transfer from a pasted-in strip in the cavity mold. There are advantages and disadvantages to both techniques. The latter system allows for changing the pattern, but may come loose and not wear satisfactorily. The first method is more durable and is the usual procedure for series moldings, but commits the builder to one particular design because changing a cavity is expensive.

The patterns which are used generally come from embossed, flexible plastic or thin metal sheets cemented to the plug or cavity.

One of the earliest transfer patterns, interestingly enough, came from an embossed vinyl sheet which had been designed as an overlay for steel decks on Navy ships. It went under the trade name of Dexolium. Many sailboats were produced with this molded-in pattern used for decking. Unfortunately, while the grip was good, it was hard to make a perfect transfer molding and the cleaning characteristics were poor.

Fiberglass has greatly replaced the use of canvas for covering decks. It will be noted that many new boats of wood construction are treated in this fashion. The glass-resin covering is more durable and is rot proof. If the covering is punctured or ripped it can easily be patched.

Fiberglass deck covering is used widely today on the decks of wooden hulls, on plywood decks of limited series glass hulls and, occasionally, on steel decks of pleasure boats. In principle, the process is to create a thin molded glass skin that bonds to the deck structure and makes a protective, watertight seal and a durable surface. One layer of glass cloth is usually sufficient for plywood. Two layers may be necessary on a planked deck, depending on its soundness and possible expansion and contraction.

Three methods of providing an anti-skid character have been used. The first has fallen into disuse because it is hard to control the uniformity and the traction is not really satisfactory. This system involves a minimum application of resin to the cloth so that the square grid pattern leaves a rough surface.

The second method is to apply an alkyd or epoxy paint containing an anti-skid compound to the smooth lamination of cloth and resin. This system is easy to carry out and the results are effective.

The third method involves mixing the standard anti-skid compound into the final coat of resin. The writer prefers this technique because color and skid-proofness are integrally bonded into the lamination. Any painting system does not last as long. An additional advantage is the fact that the anti-skid grit serves as a reinforcement to the surface coat of resin which might be flowed on too thickly or, for a number of reasons, might have a tendency to shrink and craze. This latter point brings forth the suggestion that no more resin should ever be applied to the cloth than is necessary to fill the pattern and give a smooth plane.

Other variations of this technique are used, such as sprinkling pumice or sand on the final wet resin coat and then dusting off the excess after cure. This gives a high traction surface, but it is hard to distribute the compound evenly.

Covering a cabin top or deck with fiberglass is not very different from applying canvas. It is true the glass cloth will not stretch, but a standard glass boat cloth forms extremely well around contours. Moldings and fittings should be removed, and a clean and dry wood surface prepared. When applying glass to a wide planked deck it may be necessary to lay down a double layer of cloth in order to allow for expansion and contraction. In the case of very old decks that are loaded with paint, and possibly gouged and rutted, it may be more practical to first lay down waterproof Masonite or plywood in order to give a proper flat surface to laminate the fiberglass.

CHAPTER 8

Spars

ALUMINUM SPARS are about as universally accepted for modern sailboats as fiberglass is for sailboat hulls. However, enough usage has been made of glass masts and booms that the application does deserve recognition and discussion.

Resilience, strength and design freedom are the essential advantages which fiberglass has to offer, but the low modulus of stiffness is the biggest problem. At this date the most successful examples have been small, light rigs in some cases unstayed which have taken best advantage of the intrinsic properties.

Some examples of glass spars produced in the 1940's are of interest, and their performances do point up some of the engineering problems. Bill Tritt, founder of the Glasspar Boat Co., was perhaps the earliest experimenter. He laminated glass masts for a small sloop, the Kitten, which had a stayed rig, and later unstayed spars on a salty little 20' cat ketch called the Privateer. On the East Coast, Marscot Boat Co. produced glass masts for the Rhodes designed 13' Wood Pussy. Raymond Creekmore, of Miami, was one of the first builders of glass auxiliaries in the 36'- to 40'-range and produced both masts and booms in glass for his limited series hulls. Fred Coleman's first 40' fiberglass Bounty sloops, produced in 1956, were probably the most notable large hulls to feature glass spars. A few of these early glass Bountys still retain their glass masts, but most are now equipped with aluminum.

These early experimenters proved that fiberglass spars could be produced by simple molding techniques but, by and large, all the glass masts demonstrated an important deficiency that became particularly critical when the boats entered competition. The glass masts had too much flexibility. When the spar molders attempted to correct for this condition by increasing wall thickness and section, the fiberglass spar became too heavy.

All these early glass spars were basically constructed with the same reinforcing materials used in counterpart glass hulls. The specific modulus of stiffness was therefore roughly one-third that of aluminum or less, depending on the glass to resin ratio selected. The Bounty masts, for instance, were constructed entirely of bi-directional woven roving, about 70 per cent by weight, in a clam shell cavity mold employing a pressure bag insert to densify the glass.

Note fiber orientation and hardware mounting on Sabot's spars.

What appears to be new on the scene now are manufacturing techniques which increase the stiffness factor to a marked degree and also a spar and sail rig design which takes advantage of the tough, elastic properties available in a well-developed glass laminate. The spars shown in this article are for small, simple designs, but they may be the forerunners of larger and more heavily stressed masts. We suspect that the thought and care going into these small sailing rigs can build a foundation of knowledge and experience which may be applied to larger ones. It is also quite apparent that in recent years there has been a great deal of empirical research and experimentation going on in sail design. This is now extending into spar innovations, particularly in respect to the "bendy" variety.

There are two companies engineering glass spars for the small fiberglass sailboats pictured here: the Industrial Micarta Division of Westinghouse Electric Corp. and the Silaflex Division of Browning Arms Co.

Westinghouse is using a filament winding process on their spars. The actual boom and mast assemblies are currently distributed by the Angus-Campbell Co. of Los Angeles and have been successfully employed on W. D. Schock's Sabot sailing dinghy. The Silaflex Division of Browning produces a pre-impregnated fiberglass cloth wrap spar which is the same basic process that the company has used on its fishing rods, vaulting poles, archery equipment and so on. Silaflex glass spars are currently being used on W. D. Schock's Sabot as well as the Kite and Flipper designs being manufactured by the Newport Boat Division of Browning Arms. In the Flipper, the tiller and hiking stick are also of the same fiberglass construction.

Reportedly, one of the best features about the glass spars on these little craft is the almost complete elimination of breakage. The boats are most commonly sailed by small fry and they administer plenty of abuse

A W. D. Schock Sabot fitted with an Angus-Campbell fiberglass mast and boom assembly

and mishandling. The glass spars are enormously elastic, just like a fiberglass fishing rod. They yield considerably beyond what an equivalent aluminum or wooden mast will, but have a perfect "memory." Another provocative feature from a sail design standpoint is the taper of section and wall thickness which provides a flex curve along the spar's whole effective length. Westinghouse claims that this helps contribute to a 25 per cent weight saving over the wooden spar originally used on the Sabot.

Both the Silaflex and Westinghouse glass spar processes have a high reproducibility factor. That is to say, each unit bends the same, thereby making it much easier for the sailmaker to insure good, consistent performance.

Maintenance on these fiberglass spars, of course, is virtually nil and minor repairs should be easy to do with ordinary glass-resin materials. Standard hardware is used to a large extent, but the drilling of holes for

Dinghy spar being developed by spiral wrapping glass tape over paper form.

Jean Filloux

fittings in high stress areas of the mast must be avoided. As in the case of aluminum mast extrusions, slugs of foam are inserted to provide positive buoyancy to the spar and prevent a capsized centerboard hull from going all the way over.

The Westinghouse and Silaflex processes for manufacturing spars involve rather expensive tooling and equipment relative to what has been employed in the past. A precisely machined steel mandrel is the basic form over which the impregnated fiberglass is wrapped and oriented.

Raymond Creekmore sits astride a molded fiberglass boom designed for his Captiva Class auxiliaries. Creekmore develops his spars by wrapping glass cloth around a light, supporting core.

Owens-Corning

Cat-Ketch by Bill Tritt, Glasspar Co,, features unstayed glass masts. An early, successful rig.

Epoxy resin is used as the laminating resin to provide the desired measure of strength, stiffness and interlaminate adhesion. A mechanical system of laying the fiberglass on the mandrel insures close control of thickness, fiber distribution and orientation.

To date, spar sections up to about 25 feet in length have been produced. The two manufacturers feel that it is feasible to splice longer sections together, but could not recount actual experience yet with this proposed method. They also feel that the tooling and process can be expanded to much larger continuous spar length, say, in the 40- and 60-ft. range. To this concept we end up with more questions than answers since the mandrels are expensive and the volume in any one size of larger spars is quite limited. Perhaps the spar manufacturing technique which Westinghouse and Silaflex are exhibiting presently is most suitable for small, simple one-design sailboats.

The interest for using glass in spars at this time seems to involve two separate and distinct objectives. On the one hand, older one-design classes which have converted their hulls from wood to fiberglass but have retained their wooden spars are looking for a better material substitute. Not the least of the problem is the fact that good spruce is very hard to obtain today.

The other faction would like to see whether a more efficient sailing rig can be developed around the particular properties obtainable in a laminated glass spar. It would seem that the Kite and possibly the Finn are suitable examples.

Aspects on Safety

The collapse or failure of a mast, particularly a large one, can be extremely dangerous. The writer feels that the way in which a glass spar lets go exhibits safety features which are important. An unusual accident which we are familiar with illustrates the point.

A 40' Bounty sloop with a glass mast and a 33' Galaxy sloop with an aluminum mast had a peculiar collision under full sail. They collided in such a fashion that their upper rigging became entangled and took the major force rather than the hulls. The Bounty's glass mast broke about six feet down the trunk. The Galaxy aluminum mast let go just above the main halyard winch. The way each material failed is the important point. The glass spar simply bent beyond its yield point and collapsed like a shattered bamboo pole, and the fibers of glass held the broken piece from detaching and falling to the deck. After bending a considerable distance, the aluminum spar snapped off leaving sharp, ragged edges.

Upon examination of the broken members it was significant that the glass spar had collapsed without any dangerous flailing action, and the edges of the broken pieces were not sharp. The glass strands, with resin split away, were much like a cut piece of hemp rope.

Building A Fiberglass Spar

There is no reason why the interested amateur craftsman should not attempt the construction of a fiberglass spar for a small day sailer. In the case of larger masts, say over 30' in length, the stresses and strains are such that professional abilities are probably required. It is doubtless already apparent to the reader that design data are relatively limited and such work that has been done to date has been based on trial and error experimentation.

For the interested individual we have some suggestions on how to proceed in the construction of a lightweight spar. If you have had little or no experience with fiberglassing procedures, don't try a mast until you have refined your techniques a bit on a less critical member such as a

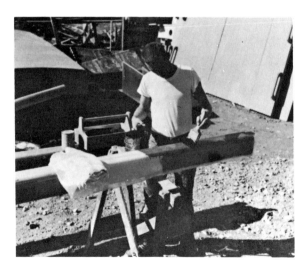

Glass sheathing being applied to wooden box spar for forty foot Newporter ketch.

Newport Fiberglass Boats

Alcort Flying fish has successfully demonstrated the
virtues of a flexible fiberglass mast with full batten sail.

spinnaker pole or boom. As far as molding techniques go, consider using
a cardboard mailing tube or some similar core as your form. Spiral wrap
this form with glass tape, butting the edges and crisscrossing the layers of
tape. Resin can be applied with a brush after each layer of tape has been
wound and secured. Additional layers of glass must be built up where
hardware is to be installed.

Fiberglassing Wooden Spars

Covering a wooden spar with glass and resin has proven quite
popular, and it has many merits. Generally it is done on a hollow, box-
type spar in order to provide a more durable surface and, by virtue of the
high tensile strength of the glass fiber, to bind the wooden members
together with greater security. Glass wrapping of a solid spar, however,
should be approached with greater care. The larger mass of wood exerts
considerable expansion force. This can be accommodated by completely
sealing out moisture and adding extra glass reinforcement when and
where expansion movement is known to be of considerable magnitude.

While glass is usually applied to a spar principally as a protective
covering and only secondarily for strength, it is felt that the basic system
could be carried further to the development of a truly efficient composite
structure. Wood can be used as the mold form and basic compression
bearing member. Properly designed glass sheathing would complement
the wood by increasing bending strength and stiffness.

CHAPTER 9

Mufflers and Exhaust Tubes

FIBERGLASS EXHAUST TUBES have been widely used in auxiliary sailboats and inboard powerboats for a number of years, but the development of marine mufflers in fiberglass was a more recent innovation. Because metal has for so long been accepted as the logical material in this type of application, it is quite significant that a new material like fiberglass can fulfill the performance requirements. Experience so far with exhaust assemblies made from fiberglass-reinforced plastics has shown important advantages over their metal counterparts.

Suitability of material

The basic properties of fiberglass-plastic are well suited to this application. The material, of course, is corrosionproof—perhaps its most singular advantage over metal mufflers and tubes. Weight saving is another advantage, particularly in the case of large mufflers. Fiberglass reinforced plastic is a much better sound dampener than metal, as has been tested and demonstrated with motor shrouds, housings and other similar industrial uses.

Adequate heat resistance is a logical point to raise. The majority of marine engines are water-cooled, drawing water from the outside and discharging it through the exhaust system. This constant flow of water maintains a very modest temperature at the point where the mufflers and exhaust tubes are located. The heat in this area is about 130°, well within the tolerable limits of an ordinary fiberglass-plastic laminate.

One question, of course, arises. What happens if the water pump should fail and uncooled hot gases are forced through the fiberglass exhaust system? In the case of such a malfunction, the fiberglass components will have sufficient heat resistance to hold up as long as the engine will continue to run without cooling. Rubber mufflers have been used successfully for some time, and rubber has a lower heat resistance than any fiberglass laminate.

Fiberglass-plastics have been tried in dry-muffler systems for automotive and truck engines, but sustained temperatures up to 1200° eventually break down the resin. However, improvements in the heat resistance of resinous binders for glass are being made and perhaps in a few years the solution will be forthcoming.

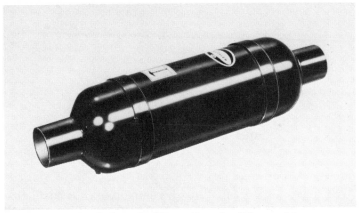

Vernay Products furnishes a line of widely accepted fiberglass mufflers and exhaust tubes.

Cost savings and performance advantages have been shown with fiberglass exhaust tubes. The extent to which such tubing is utilized will vary with the type of power installation. Generally the assembly involves a conventional iron manifold leading into heavy reinforced rubber tube. At the cold end of the system where rigid members are common, fiberglass tube sections are employed. This is to say, elbows and through-hull pieces are molded fiberglass.

The fiberglass through-hull portions have worked out well. From an installation standpoint they are of simple, unitized construction. No special flanges of fastenings are necessary. They will not corrode and stain the transom. From a safety standpoint, the through-hull tube is bonded to the hull in such an integral manner that it is only remotely possible that an accident could cause leakage.

This particular point was proven to the writer on observing what happened to some powerboats damaged in a hurricane a few years ago. In one harbor several wooden hulls were sunk because their projecting exhaust tubes were smashed and the flange fitting wrenched free so that water entered. A fiberglass powerboat involved in the identical circumstances did not sink; although the projecting end of the tube was sheared off, the bond to the transom did not break.

Fiberglass exhaust systems currently developed offer some real improvements in performance and dependability. The material is tough, durable and free from corrosion. It is efficiently light in weight and has inherently good sound-dampening properties. The combination of favorable material costs and ease of fabrication mean a substantial saving over metal construction.

CHAPTER 10

Fuel and Water Tanks

WATER AND FUEL TANKS of fiberglass construction are being used extensively today. They are particularly common in glass auxiliaries and power cruisers where the builder has chosen to extend the usage of the material to many other component parts besides the hull and deck structure.

The proper and safe containment of fluids on board any vessel is an important matter. For this reason, and because glass plastic tanks are relatively new, it is worthwhile to discuss the application in some detail. The boat owner should understand how to regard such tanks—what care should be given and what comprises a good installation.

Performance and Design Advantages

In the writer's opinion a well-built and properly installed fiberglass tank will give superior, trouble-free performance for the life of the craft. There will be no rust, scale or corrosion to contaminate the contents or, for that matter, any other type of material deterioration which might obstruct the fuel or water system. Molded construction eliminates the typical type of seam found in metal tanks, which can be the source of fatigue cracks and leakage.

From a design point of view, there are a number of unique advantages which the naval architect can effectively utilize. First of all, there is a material weight saving. A fiberglass tank can be as much as 50 to 60 percent lighter than a comparable steel model. This factor can be of real importance in the high-speed power cruisers where large fuel tankage is required.

The ease of forming irregular shapes in fiberglass means that tanks can be readily developed to fit any usable area in the hull. For this reason, we find many sailing auxiliaries so equipped.

Fiberglass water tanks are often made integral with the fiberglass hull structure. That is, the hull surface may serve as one or two walls for the tank. When the designer is able to make such tanks perform multiple functions, the greatest advantages are apparent. Integral construction may offer a number of efficient structural and weight-distribution features; for instance, water tankage can be provided below the floors of a keel sailboat hull—an area which is ordinarily unusable in a wooden hull. The tank walls themselves may perform various functions, such as structural stiffening, support for engine bearers, bunks, and other accommodation elements.

The natural resilience and impact resistance of the fiberglass material have proven a valuable property in service, as evidenced in several cases of collisions where the fiberglass tanks absorbed tremendous shock without rupturing. If repairs to a fiberglass fuel tank are necessary they can be done with much greater ease than with a metal type. No laborious steaming or purging of the contents is necessary since a glass resin patch can be applied without open flame or high heat.

A fiberglass laminate is a much better thermal insulator than metals. For this reason it has been found that such tanks substantially reduce internal water condensation. And, the translucent properties of a fiberglass laminate can often eliminate the need for a fuel gauge. In summary, it can be seen that through fiberglass construction the designer has been freed from past material limitation to impart more functional and efficient tankage arrangements.

Materials and Construction Methods

The same basic glass and resin materials used in the construction of the molded hull are suitable for tank fabrication. However, there are some special considerations. Fire retardant polyester resin is generally authorized for fuel tank construction. In the case of water tanks, care must be exercised with the resin and catalyst system so that residual taste in the water is not present.

The fiberglass reinforcements used in the construction of marine water and fuel tanks are, of course, virtually inert to any attack. The same types of glass materials are used in the tanks or in the hull or deck structure, but the exact choice of chopped fibers or fabric varies according to construction technique and design. Molding methods vary somewhat according to design, volume undertaken and fabricator preferences. Where simple shape and large volume are involved, high-pressure, matched-die molding systems can be employed. For complicated forms or short runs, simple contact-molding techniques are used. In the latter case, vacuum bag pressure is sometimes applied as a method to insure that pin holes or voids are thoroughly worked out of the laminate.

With regard to process methods, note the accompanying photograph on the Apex tank-molding system. It is somewhat unique, and their centrifugal casting process turns out a tank with extremely good laminate uniformity and fine finished appearance. The Apex firm uses this system to manufacture truck fuel tanks, water-softener tanks and torpedo tubes for the Navy. The company also has a line of these cylindrical tanks for marine use.

Due to the critical nature of a gasoline fuel tank we feel strongly that it is not a project for the amateur builder. Because an individual has successfully molded some small parts, or perhaps fiberglassed a wooden hull or deck, he cannot assume that he has the necessary skill and knowledge to do a good job on a gas tank. Proper design, the quality of the laminate and correct installation of the fittings are highly important.

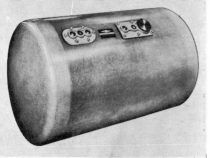

Centrifugally cast fiberglass tank by Apex Fiberglass Products. Pressure formed end caps are fused to the seamless molded tank barrel.

Photos from Apex Fiberglass Products

Beyond this, all fuel tanks must be thoroughly pressure tested before installation—a procedure which is not easily handled by the average mechanic in a simply equipped shop.

Water tanks, on the other hand, are suitable do-it-yourself projects. The application is not critical. In a following chapter we will describe in detail just how to construct a fresh-water tank with fiberglass and resin materials.

Is There Any Danger of Leakage?

Poor design and construction can possibly lead to a leakage problem. A pinhole in the laminate, a poorly fabricated seam, or an incorrectly bonded fitting could be sources of trouble. However, when such tanks have been constructed by an experienced molder, no problems should be anticipated. The glass-resin laminate is not going to deteriorate and develop a leak at a later date.

Well-built fiberglass tanks have turned in a good performance record under unusually severe conditions. One builder recounts the case of a 12-gallon auxiliary gas tank which broke loose from its mounting in a fishing skiff. The sea was so rough that the heavily loaded tank could not be immediately secured and it slammed around the cockpit for more than an hour. The fiberglass tank did not burst or spill its contents during this rough treatment. In another case, we inspected a wedge-shaped fiberglass fuel tank which was mounted in the bow section of a boat that had collided head-on with another craft. The bow of the boat was completely crushed and the condition of the damage showed clearly that the fiberglass tank had absorbed a large part of the impact with only a minor crack at its leading edge.

While such case histories give testimony to the high impact strength and ruggedness of the material, one should not be led to think that these tanks are indestructible or that severe blows might not cause trouble. Because of its resilience, a severe impact will not dent the laminate as in the case of metal, but it might cause a "local star craze" that could result in

Diesel fuel oil tankage is integrally formed in Halmatic fiberglass power boat hull. Compartments will be sealed with fiberglass or aluminum cover plates.

Halmatic Ltd.

an incipient leak. Fortunately any condition such as this can be easily repaired with a glass-resin patch. In most instances it is not necessary to drain and air the tank as would be required when welding or brazing a ruptured metal fuel tank.

Separate Versus Integral Fuel Tanks

As we have stated, fiberglass construction has made possible the incorporation of integral tankage in small craft. Some debate has existed over the safety of integral gasoline containment in fiberglass hulls. The primary reservation has been the dangerous consequences resulting from a collision and rupture of the fuel cell. It is hard to say what formal regulation will eventually result on this matter, but there are some

One hundred and fifty gallon custom fabricated fiberglass fuel tank. Note baffle installation. Lid will be fiberglass bonded.

Hatteras Yacht Co.

101

practical guides for consideration. An integral gasoline tank can be designed in such a manner as to be quite safe and functional. One popular class of fiberglass auxiliaries has gasoline tankage provided below the cabin sole. In this position the tanks are protected by the keel and heavy dead wood section, and the possibility of rupture is extremely remote. Several of these yachts have experienced severe gounding without any detrimental effects to the tanks. However, the writer does take exception to certain integral fuel-tank installations seen in fiberglass outboard designs. Some such craft have gas tanks which are built into the side of the hull shell. The danger here is that wracking of the hull or an impact might rupture the tank.

Regulatory bodies in this country, such as the Coast Guard, insurance authorities and yacht surveyors are more disposed towards the approval of separate gasoline fuel tanks. However, it is probable that a different classification of approval will eventually come about concerning integral designs.

Regulatory Standards & Specifications

The U.S. Coast Guard has approved fiberglass fuel tanks for gasoline and diesel powered commercially operated motor craft. While the Coast Guard does not as yet regulate tank construction practice on pleasure boats, they may at some time in the future under the Boat Safety Act enacted in 1971.

The Coast Guard and industry members recognize the standards and recommendations published by the American Boat & Yacht Council (15 East 26th Street, New York, N.Y. 10010). Recommendations on fuel tanks and fuel systems as a whole have been developed by this organization.

Cost and Availability

For one wishing to purchase a fiberglass fuel or water tank for his boat, there are two sources. Many of the fiberglass boat builders, particularly those molding auxiliaries and inboards, are able and willing to furnish custom tanks or perhaps provide one from stock. More recently some fabricators have gone into the business of making tanks for stock boat builders and for retail sale.

The prices of these fiberglass tanks appear to be considerably less than the premium Monel metal type, but somewhat more expensive than those of conventional galvanized steel.

Tank Taste

If the laminating resin used in fresh-water tanks is not properly cured, the taste imparted to the water can be disagreeable, although not harmful. A cup of hot tea brewed from water from such a tank is a taste treat not easily forgotten, but totally unnecessary to endure. The error occurs in the manufacture of the tank, where the resin and catalyst system must be properly matched so that a complete cure is effected.

Experience shows that properly made fiberglass water tanks will keep their contents pure and taste free.

Boat owners who would like to correct an annoying taste condition have the choice of several practical remedies. For a very mild condition, flushing out with fresh water several times will be effective. A rather strong solution of baking soda allowed to stand in the tank for several hours has also proven helpful. The best and most effective method, however, is the introduction of live steam to the tank. The steam can be provided by any makeshift apparatus and allowed to circulate through the tank for several hours. In effect, the steam heat cures the laminate and purges the excess styrene monomer.

Are There Special Installation Procedures?

Fiberglass fuel tanks of a non-integral type are installed in the identical manner as their metal counterparts. Details of venting, grounding and proper support are as important in the installation of fiberglass tanks as with metal ones. Since fill and feed-line fittings on fiberglass tanks are usually the conventional cast-bronze type, no special adaptors are necessary. Because rust and corrosion are not problems, liberties can be taken with the usual air space factor required.

Fuel-level gauges are not always necessary when installing fiberglass tanks. Since even a color-pigmented laminate has considerable translucency, a positive, visual check on the fluid level is therefore available at all times. If the tank can be mounted in such a position that its side wall can be easily observed, there is no real need for a fuel gauge.

Because of the present status of formal regulations in the pleasure boat industry, a certain burden of personal responsibility is placed on the owner if he is to be sure that important items such as the fuel system are assembled to appropriate high standards.

CHAPTER 11

Repairs to Fiberglass Boats

THE EASE OF MAKING structural repairs on a fiberglass boat is one of the material's major advantages; in fact, it is one of the chief reasons fiberglass construction is so widely used for Army, Navy and Coast Guard boats. Unskilled personnel in the field have proved fully capable of quickly restoring a damaged boat to serviceable condition.

The exact procedure for dealing with such repairs is well covered in various instruction booklets put out by some boatbuilders and raw-material manufacturers. We will cover here a number of special points which will help owners to properly evaluate a repair job when misfortune strikes.

Unique Material Characteristics

The simplicity of fiberglass repairs results from two material features—the manner in which it breaks and the way such damaged material can be restored. A fiberglass panel is very resilient; it will either yield and recover when hit by a severe blow or it will break decisively, leaving localized damage. There is no denting or distortion, no long, splintered members to remove and replace.

Mending a broken fiberglass panel is most similar, perhaps, to patching a rubber tire or rebuilding a molded wooden shell with glue and veneer strips. The same resin and glass materials used in the construction of the boat are employed in the repair. No complicated tools or equipment are required. To make a good, strong repair, however, reasonable care and a planned procedure are necessary.

Some Important Points to Observe

Perhaps of first consideration is that the area to be mended must be dry and clean and the available temperature high enough to allow the resin to harden. If the weather is cool (below 70°), inexpensive infra-red bulbs are a perfect answer for raising the surface temperature and making the resin cure properly.

If the break is large or rather complex, spend some time studying the situation. Because of the nature of the material there are usually a number of satisfactory ways to make a good repair. As a rule, however, there will be an "easier" approach which will come to mind after a little thought.

To aid in such deliberation, it would be highly worthwhile to refer to a repair manual on fiberglass before proceeding with the job.

Repair can be handled from the inside or outside. It is customary on hulls to build up fresh material largely on the interior where any unevenness of the patch will be relatively invisible. Decks present a special problem in this regard because of the difficult working position and are usually worked from the outside.

It is not necessary to remove all the fractured material involved in the rupture, although some prefer to do so. Leaving some sound but jagged pieces may help materially in giving a substantial form or area on which to build up a new laminate.

The main objective in any repair is to restore the laminate thickness and overall strength continuity. To do this, the most effective and neat method is to generously bevel-grind the area adjacent to the hole or fracture and then lay up layers of resin-impregnated glass until the original thickness is achieved. If the break occurs in a critical area, or if there is any question about the strength of a patch, additional overlapping plies can be added for insurance.

How Strong Is a Repair Patch?

If a fiberglass patch is properly applied, that is to say, good materials, good workmanship and an adequate scarf-bonding area furnished, the repair will be substantially equal to the original strength. Since the bond with the older surface is the critical point, its preparation is important. It must be clean, dry and rough sanded.

The damaged area can easily be "beefed up" and made as strong as desired by simply adding additional and relatively large overlapping plies of material, as shown in the accompanying repair diagram.

Extensive Damage

There is hardly any damage which cannot be repaired, but of course, there are practical limits—limits largely defined by the economics of time and labor, not the workability of the material. Early in our experiments with fiberglass boat construction we investigated the repairability of extensively damaged hulls. One case involved the restoration of a 15' hull that was battered in a hurricane and given up as a total loss. There were three large holes in the bottom and fully one-quarter of one side was missing.

An ambitious fellow acquired the derelict and with some qualified instruction, plus patience and diligence, rebuilt the boat to like-new condition. He had never used fiberglass materials before, but he was a good mechanic and was willing to expend the necessary time and effort. Of course it is rare that an individual would take on as big a project as this. The question is usually whether the manufacturer or qualified repair yard can handle such work.

A number of case histories show that badly damaged fiberglass boats have been rebuilt at substantially less than replacement cost.

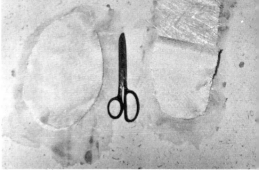

Two five-inch breaks in dinghy hull shown from outside (left). From the interior, fractures have been scarfed and sanded, and fiberglass cloth and mat patches cut to size (right).

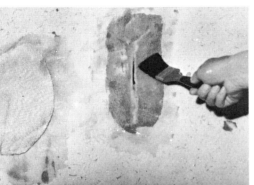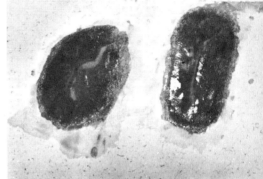

Prime coat of resin is applied to break (left), and patches have been saturated with resin (right). Finishing will require sanding and paint to match inside of hull. Small slots on outside of hull should be filled with glass and matching resin.

Possibly one of the best examples was written up by Vincent Bamford of Liberty Mutual Insurance Co. in the December 1961 issue of YACHTING. This 32′ auxiliary was badly holed and mauled during a 1960 hurricane. The boat was auctioned off at a price representing her running gear, which was in good shape, and other fixed equipment. A knowledgeable builder bought the boat, rebuilt her for about $1500 and sold her for a handsome profit. As Mr. Bamford describes it, the restored vessel was as good as new and the repair joints not discernible.

Big fractures and holes have been rare with fiberglass hulls. Cases of major damage have largely resulted from collision or hurricane disasters. At this time only a few dealers and yards are able to cope with such big repairs, so the boat usually goes back to the factory. The situation, however, is improving as more and more yards are becoming familiar with the material.

It might interest the reader to know the alternate means by which big repairs are often handled. If a large panel in the boat is knocked out, it is necessary to have some kind of a mold form for that area clamped temporarily in place so that a new fair laminate can be built up. With relatively small holes, say up to two feet in diameter, a temporary backing

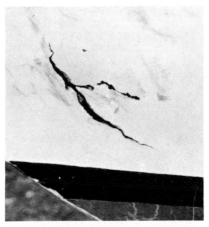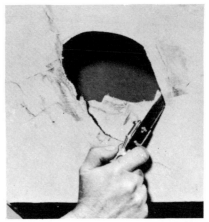

Break in bow of hull (left) is prepared for patching by sawing away fractured pieces to the sound part of the laminate (right).

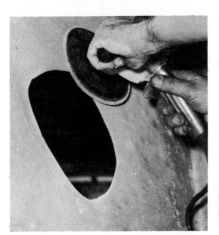

Working from the inside, the hole is feather-sanded (left) with a coarse disc. Right, a cardboard back plate is placed over the hole and fresh material is applied from the inside.

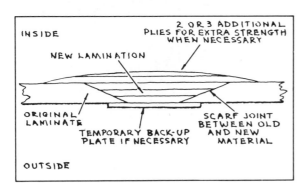

Repair Patch in Cross Section: Required scarf angle varies with thickness; 8:1 for relatively thin laminates up to 3/16"; 16:1 for 1/4" and above. Thin shell laminates, about 1/8", need extra overlapping plies, providing at least 25% increase in thickness.

107

plate can be readily formed out of a soft metal, like aluminum, or perhaps even of cardboard. However, if the hole is larger than this or the break involves complex contours, it may be best to procure a cast cavity section from the master mold in the builder's shop. This facsimile section from the mold is bolted over the ruptured area and the repair implemented from the inside of the boat.

In other instances, small boats with very large holes have been simply placed back in the original cavity mold and the entire laminate continuity re-established. A case study of this type is shown in the Owens-Corning repair guide.

Temporary Repairs

A question that often arises is how to cope with emergency damage situations which might occur at sea or in some remote spot on a cruise.

Photos from Owens-Corning

Complex break at the shear line (above left) involving hull and section of the deck.

The hole is sawed out cleanly (above right) and an aluminum sheet is formed to approximate contour and will be taped in place.

(Right) Finished patch preparatory to painting. Surface is fair and smooth.

Quite specifically, a number of fiberglass-boat owners going into Bermuda Races ask what kind of a fiberglass repair kit should be taken along. Structural damage due to collision or grounding are perhaps the two extreme emergencies to be considered.

The foresighted skipper going far from shore has always provided his boat with a stock of spare parts and the necessary materials for emergency repairs to the hull. The fiberglass boat owner should be no exception. He should avail himself of a repair kit of glass and resin. These kits can be purchased from a marine hardware store or plastics supply house. Here is what we suggest in the way of essential contents:

Fiberglass cloth— several square yards.

Fiberglass tape 6" wide—10 yards.

Polyester resin—at least a quart in pint cans.

Fiberglass mat—one square yard.

Epoxy cement—several tubes.

The cloth and mat would be largely useful for taking care of a fracture or hole. The tape is enormously useful— perhaps for restoring a fractured spar or temporarily stopping a leak in a pipe or the cold end of the exhaust tube. Polyester resin would be easiest to handle under field conditions because it will wet the glass rapidly and cure more quickly than epoxy. The epoxy cement can be considered as a "super" glue or solder and has many obvious applications.

Accidents don't always occur in such a convenient way that this recommended repair kit can be immediately employed. That is to say, you can't apply a patch to the hull when you are rolling around in a sea or when it's raining and cold. You may have to apply some ingenuity and special techniques to protect the watertight integrity of the boat until you can get into a sheltered spot, and then use the fiberglass repair materials. Such techniques have been employed by seamen for generations—stuffing the hole with a rag, pillow or mattress is one example; a collision mat is another. It would even be possible in certain circumstances to drill through the fiberglass hull and bolt in place a make-shift dam con-

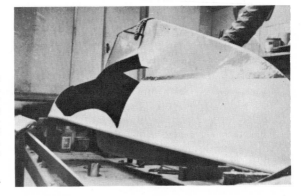

This 12' keel sailboat was damaged in a hurricane. Twenty-five percent of her hull was knocked out but restored at less than replacement cost by placing the hull back in the mold. Even with this area loss, the form remained true.

Cape Cod Shipbuilding Co.

structed from any available wooden member in the boat. Such measures have been successfully employed where lives were at stake.

In the case of small craft like an outboard or a dinghy which has a rip or hole, waterproof pressure-sensitive tape will hold up surprisingly well. We have successfully depended on such tape repairs when running canoes through rocky rapids where the hull is often punctured and we didn't want to spend the time doing a permanent job.

Within the limitations expressed above, emergency repairs are easy to do on a fiberglass boat. Last summer we talked to a fiberglass auxiliary owner who, while on a cruise, had been rammed by another boat. The break was amidships, above the waterline, about two inches wide by a foot long. He made a temporary but effective repair with fiberglass materials. The job was unsighly, but it was strong and kept the water out. He lost only a few hour's time on his vacation cruise; and, as a matter of fact, sailed the boat the rest of the summer in this condition, leaving the finishing touches on the repair to be done after hauling for the winter.

Crazing—Surface Crack Repairs

The most aggravating misfortune which has occurred in fiberglass boats concerns fine cracks that sometimes appear in the outer coat of resin. The following will deal with the subject in detail and show a case study in repair which will provide guidance to fiberglass boat owners who may have to cope with a similar problem.

The smooth, colored exterior of most fiberglass hulls is provided by a layer of polyester resin called a "gel coat." Since glass boats are molded "inside out," this exterior coat is applied first in the cavity mold lay-up procedures. The resin is applied with brush or spray gun, usually the latter. The resinous coat is many times thicker than an ordinary coat of paint about .013", and by its nature is not directly reinforced with glassfiber. This means that the gel coat must take a lot of abuse—abrasion, impact, exposure to sunlight and water. The polyester resin is high resistant to these elements, but one cannot assume that the plastic will hold its fresh, shining appearance indefinitely. This is why fiberglass hulls must be painted after a period of years. It is, essentially, a matter of appearance and the life of the gel coat.

What we are now concerned with are unsightly cracks or crazing, which appear in the surface gel coat. This is a premature failure of the surface resin because a good gel coat, although it may fade or become chalky after a number of years, will not crack. The craze or crack condition is due to a poorly formulated or poorly applied gel coat. The resin is basically the same as in the body of the laminate, but it is compounded differently to provide somewhat special features; i.e., hardness for gloss retention, impact resistance, hiding power, and so on. Since long-lasting gloss is obtained from a rather hard resin that tends to be brittle, and impact resistance is gained from a softer, more elastic resin, it can be seen that the formulation has to be somewhat of a compromise. The reader will not be too interested in the fine points of what causes the craze condition, but he will want to know how to regard the condition and how it can be fixed.

The cracks, small or large, do not indicate a deterioration in the laminate of the boat. The fissures extend only to the glass-reinforced portion—and stop there. They might, of course, be associated with a damage impact or a rupture, but such cases would be quite obvious.

The pattern of occurrence, or location, is not easily defined except in a general way. A spotty case on a deck is most often due to improper thickness control of the gel coat. Deck moldings may have sharp radii where the resin becomes excessively thick and shrinkage cracks occur. If crazing is extensive on a hull, the cause is probably a poorly compounded gel coat. Thin panels which are prone to flexing or "oil-canning" may be more susceptible to crazing but this is not always true.

Crazing generally shows up in the first or second year after the boat is molded, if it is going to occur at all.

A Case History and Repair Technique

The accompanying photographs are before and after pictures of a fiberglass pram which became very badly cracked. We had never seen such a severe condition, and it presented an ideal challenge to show how restoration could be done. The pram is of an excellent design, strong and well-built, but the surface coat of resin was not properly formulated or applied. The age of the hull was about nine years. The cracks had been evident since the first year or so and had gradually extended over the entire surface. In some places there were only hair-line fissures, but many wide cracks crisscrossed the surface.

Upon inspecting the hull closely, we found that the gel coat was excessively thick in many areas, thus aggravating, and perhaps even causing, the condition. We found that the surface resin along the chines, bilge keels and skeg was almost 3/16" thick. Unlike many other hard-chined prams, this one had a fuller shape and her flat sections were much stiffer. It was evident that flexing had nothing to do with the breakdown of a gel coat.

The repair procedure chosen was quite simple. We selected an epoxy surfacing compound to fill the cracks and re-establish a smooth, even surface. This epoxy resin product is highly filled and quite viscous. It is not really brushable. We found that a rubber squeegee was the best instrument to work the resin down in the cracks and at the same time wipe away the excess. A pint of the compound sufficed for the entire hull. It is important to note that we did no sanding prior to application of the epoxy resin. This would only have driven dust into the cracks and made it difficult to fill them properly.

After the epoxy had cured for several days, we went to work with a belt sander and leveled the surface. This operation entailed considerable labor and we recommend a heavy-duty machine that will cut fast, but is manageable in various positions.

When the sanding operation was completed there were still minor

Badly crazed and weathered surface of a fiberglass pram (left). Boat is nine years old. Hollow skeg (right) was worn through from dragging on the beach.

Treated with epoxy surfacing compound and epoxy paint, the boat looks like new. Skeg has been repaired with glass and resin, a brass half-round added to prevent further wear. Two-part epoxy compound and neoprene squeegee are shown in the photograph above left.

crevices and air pockets. We could have proceeded with another application of the surfacing compound but, not looking for perfection, we proceeded with several coats of epoxy primer that served the same function and was much easier to apply. The epoxy primers are thicker than the epoxy paints and therefore bridge and fill minor crazes and pockets. The primer leaves a flat finish, and thorough sanding after the first coat was beneficial. The final operation involved a single coat of

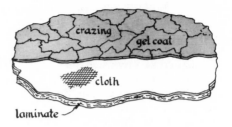

Cross-section of a fiberglass boat laminate, showing how crazing is confined to outer unreinforced layer of resin.

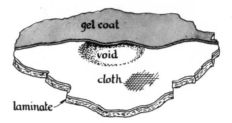

The void or air bubble behind gel coat should be cut out and filled with glass and resin. Large voids can be detected by tapping the surface over the suspected area.

epoxy paint. It provided the smooth, high-gloss finish shown in the final photos.

The repair of the skeg should be of interest to those who have a similar problem. The skeg was a hollow molding, sealed from the hull, and frequent beachings had worn it through. Several times the owner had made repairs with Epotex. Vestiges of this dark material can be seen in the second photograph. However, the Epotex only lasted a season or less. We fiberglassed the hole and built up the proper contour of the skeg with scrap pieces of glass and resin. Then a half-round brass bang strip was fastened in place. Bronze machine screws were self-tapped in the fiberglass by carefully pre-drilling the right-sized pilot hole.

We are confident that no further crazing or cracking will take place on this hull. The condition of the gel coat had just about stabilized by the time we went to work on the boat. But more important than this, the epoxy compound, by virtue of its adhesion and hardness, re-established the tough outer shell of the pram. Repainting for the sake of appearance may be necessary in another two years or so, but recurrence of cracks is only a remote possibility.

Surface Blisters

During the molding operation, occasionally, some air may become entrapped behind the gel coat and escape detection and correction at the plant. These shallow voids will vary from about 1/8" in diameter up to about the size of a fifty-cent piece. In most cases the defect will remain unnoticed until the thin shell is crushed by an impact. In others there will be a noticeable surface bubble.

The corrective procedure is essentially the same as dealing with a

113

crazing condition, with a point or two to keep in mind. If the void is quite small, it can be easily touched up with some matching resin. The initial contrast with the older surface will even out perceptably after it weathers a bit. Large, deep voids (more than 1/8" and over 1" in diameter) should be repaired in a two-step operation. Fill the cavity with a glass-reinforced resin mix, then finish off with the proper matching resin. Too thick a concentration of pure resin will tend to shrink and crack unless stabilized and reinforced with glass fiber.

The surface imperfections which have been discussed are becoming less common as materials and techniques have been improved. Today's careful builder, using quality materials, will only occasionally incur the difficulties described.

Scratches and Gouges

In the normal course of events a glass boat will accumulate surface damage which will, for sake of appearance, require attention. On boats over a year old it will not be possible to exactly match the original color (even if white) by using a gel coat repair kit. A small scratch here and there can be so treated with the color paste supplied by the builder, and will not be especially noticeable. But if the patching is extensive, it is best to use a neutral shade of polyester or epoxy putty, then sand smooth and paint. Such surface repair materials are readily available today through marine dealers.

We have seen few molded decks which have been nicked and gouged. This speaks well for the durability of the resin, as well as for the care administered by the average owner. A heavy winch handle or a mishandled anchor can strike a lethal blow. Patching can be implemented by grinding the damaged pattern down to the laminate, then applying matching resin and impressing a patch of the original transfer material. The result will not be perfect, but will be acceptable. A localized application of epoxy paint can make a neat restoration job and will not diminish the anti-skid properties appreciably.

CHAPTER 12

Extensive Repairs Are Feasible

TWO CASE HISTORIES of fiberglass hull restoration are presented to demonstrate a variety of materials and methods which can be used to rebuild very badly damaged hull and deck structures. It is not suggested that every untrained individual has the capability and zeal to handle such work. But in both cases the individuals had considerable mechanical aptitude and an enthusiasm for accepting the challenge of manual projects. Neither parties had ever done more than rudimentary work with fiberglass, but their thoroughness and well thought out procedures contributed greatly to the excellent results.

The "Greyling" Project

In the summer of 1962, Jim Caulkins started searching for a second-hand fiberglass auxiliary. He settled on the Dolphin design and located the one he wanted in Marblehead, Mass. This was **Greyling**. Negotiations for purchase proceeded, but before they were completed the auxiliary became the victim of a September gale. Caulkins was dis-

The auxiliary after restoration.

1

As she lay on the rocks after the storm.

2

Fractured hull cut open preparatory to repair.

3

couraged, but after careful consideration he decided it was a worthwhile repair project, and made an offer on the damaged boat, which was accepted.

Greyling's mooring line had chafed through and she had been cast up on the sharp rocks along shore. It happened during the night and she was brutally pounded before the tide receded and recovery operations could be carried out. Damage was largely below the water line—a big puncture, deep gouges and scratches, the rudder torn away. Below decks the salt water had made quite a mess and the Palmer engine had been completely immersed.

In order to work on the boat in the convenience of his own backyard, Jim designed and had built a simple trailer made from an old truck chassis. The rig gave him suitable mobility for the program of repair and transporting the boat to nearby water, but was not adequate for

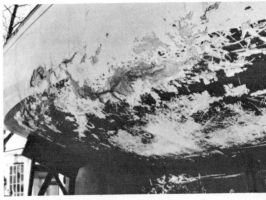

4   "Greyling" had pounded for hours on sharp rocks. Although holed through in only   5
one location (above left), the entire starboard underbody was extensively impacted and
gouged. Midship waterline area (right) suffered greatest damage. Hull shell here re-
sisted puncture but had large delaminated areas not readily apparent from outside.

6   Forefoot (left) and lead keel were gouged. Electric saber saw was used to cut away   7
damaged laminate (right).

highway towing. **Greyling** was therefore trucked by commercial carrier from Marblehead to Darien, Conn., where she was transferred to her trailer.

Cutting Into The Hull

The first step was to prepare the holed area properly to receive a patch. An electric saber saw was selected as the proper cutting tool, and fortunate indeed this was, because the final extent of cutting would have been tiring with a hand saw. The hull shell was up to 5/8" thickness in this location; this amount of fiberglass makes for tortuous going for even a heavy-capacity power saw. Metal-cutting saber blades worked best, but they wore out fast and sometimes broke. Fortunately, saber-saw blades are relatively inexpensive and quickly replaced.

The reader may wonder why such a big cut was made in the hull. The accompanying photographs, showing the original condition, indicate a much smaller hole. The reason for the large cut area is interesting and important.

While the hull shell was actually broken through in an area about 24" in diameter, extensive interply delamination had taken place all along the bilge and adjacent topside due to severe pounding on the rocks. We started with a relatively small cut around the immediate puncture, but had to keep extending the hole until the delamination condition had ceased and we were back to sound material.

This Dolphin hull was laminated with layer upon layer of heavy woven roving glass fabric. The material has very high impact resistance, but when it does yield, failure is usually in the interlaminar plane. A solid chopped strand mat laminate, on the other hand, will tend to shear perpendicularly without any interply delamination, but at a lower specific impact level.

Most of the recently molded glass hulls of this size are now built up with alternate plies of mat and woven roving which, among other advantages, tends to combine the best features of both materials.

Scarfing The Hole

When the hull shell had been cut back far enough, the edges of the hole were beveled from the inside with a heavy duty disc sander. The scarfing operation created a feather edge and a gradually sloping angle so that the new material to be applied from the inside would fair in nicely with the old. This grinding was arduous and dusty work. Jim used a respirator mask and was sure to cover himself with loose protective clothing to minimize the effects of the irritating dust. The glass-resin dust will cause no harm, but it creates varying degrees of discomfort.

When this work was completed we stepped back to appraise the situation and plan the next step. The size of the resultant hole was really a bit horrifying—over 10 feet long and up to two feet wide! Needless to say, as the cut was enlarged it was necessary to remove all the connecting and adjacent elements on the inside—a transverse bulkhead, miscellaneous joinery, the head, some through-hull connections, etc.

Another matter we were concerned about was whether removal of such a large section of the shell would cause distortion. It did not. The bottom lip of the hole sprange out perhaps 1/8", but no more. This was easily pushed back by the mold form that was subsequently applied.

Back-Up Form Needed

Small holes can be repaired by using a back-up plate made with any formable material—cardboard or aluminum sheet, for instance. However, the size of this hole and the complex contour of the missing

8   Heavy duty disk sander ground down inside edges to receive overlapping layers of   9
new material, as shown in two pictures above. Large cut in hull was necessary because of extensive delamination. Removal of big section resulted in very minor distortion to hull shell.

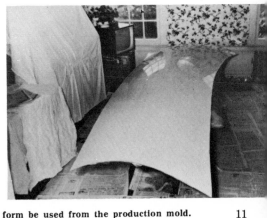

10   Size and complex shape of hole dictated that a form be used from the production mold.   11
Section corresponding to the damaged area was laminated in the master cavity at the
factory. From this form an accurate back-up mold was fabricated.

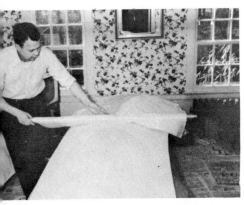

12   Application of cloth (left) and applying resin to cloth (right).   13

area dictated a more accurate method. After discussion with U. S. Yachts, builders of the boat, we ordered a section of the Dolphin hull that corresponded with the holed portion of **Greyling**. We obviously wanted a piece cast from the original plug, but because the plug was no longer available, they supplied a section laid up in the production cavity mold. Over this accurate form Caulkins was able to laminate a cavity backup piece that fitted the damaged area perfectly.

It is worth mentioning that we considered one other approach to this problem quite seriously. That was to cast a back-up form from another Dolphin. Half a dozen of these boats were in the area. However, it was the middle of winter, and eligible hulls were not really accessible for such an operation. There were many tricky details which made us discard the idea. Nevertheless, this method is feasible, particularly with smaller hulls, and it has been used successfully.

Molding The Form

As the reader probably knows, molding fiberglass requires sustained room temperature to obtain proper handling of the resin. It was the dead of winter. Jim's cellar was too small for the job and his garage without heat, so Mrs. Caulkins, who by that time was unavoidably caught up in the project, made the ultimate womanly gesture by giving up her dining room to the cause.

Photographs #12 to #16 show the lay-up of the back-up form quite well. The first step was to brush on several coats of vinyl acetate parting film. Next came a brush application of resin. A layer of glass cloth was rolled on and smoothed down evenly and tightly. After cure, successive layers of 1½oz. mat and cloth were applied until a thickness of about 3/16" was achieved. A layer of cloth and a layer of mat were impregnated at one time. The resin was poured in the middle and then worked outwards through the two materials by brush and rubber squeegee. After the final layer had set up, halved cardboard tubes were glassed over in place so that the shell form would have adequate rigidity. This same system was used on the piece that was shipped down from the factory. Photograph #16 shows a template being used to check the accuracy of the form.

The laminating of the back-up form provided useful technique training for the more difficult job on the hull itself. As some readers may know, it takes a bit of practice to learn the art of handling and impregnating glass mat.

Fitting The Form To The Hull

The finished cavity form was then mechanically fastened to the hull with several machine bolts and a dozen or so sheet metal screws. The screws were mainly useful in getting a nice tight fit.

The alignment of the cavity form was important in restoring the fair lines to the hull. This alignment was facilitated by having the boot-top

14   Tailoring glass matting to the form (left). Alternate plies of mat, a cloth layed up to a thickness of 3/16''. Working resin through cloth and mat with rubber squeegee (right).   15

16   Halved cardboard tubes are glassed in placed for stiffness (left). A template was used to check accuracy. Finished cavity form (right) was fastened over the hole with bolts and sheet metal screws.   17

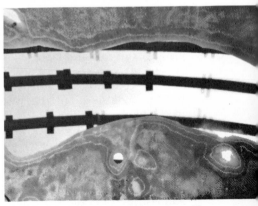

18   Precise fit was assisted by boot top scribe (left), transferred from factory mold. Right— 19 View from inside hull. Visible are scarfed laminate of hull, center round hole is from old through-hull connection, mold back-up is translucent with only stiffeners showing through.

scribe accurately transferred from the production mold to the cavity form. These relatively fine lines cannot be seen in the photograph.

Laminating The Hole

Cold weather made it impossible to do a big laminating job outside. Mrs. Caulkins' dining room was a bit too small to accommodate all of **Greyling,** although by this time pieces of the boat's anatomy were being reconditioned in almost every room in the house.

A local service station with a high ceiling and good central heating provided the perfect solution, and the entire laminating job was completed in one weekend. The boat was moved into the garage on Friday evening, and allowed to become thoroughly dry and warm preparatory to the start of work Saturday morning.

To restore the hull, three layers of woven roving, four layers of 1½ oz. mat and two layers of cloth were used. They were applied in the following manner.

The first stage was to apply two more coats of parting film to the mold face. Next came a brush coat of clear resin, then a backup of cloth. After hardening, a layer of mat and cloth were applied simultaneously. When this set up, a layer of mat and woven roving were applied together; and so on with the mat and woven roving, until the proper thickness had been established.

As each layer was applied, it overlapped the previous one by several inches, evenly fairing in with the beveled edge. The last layer of woven roving and mat was sort of an "insurance policy" and it carried a full 15" or so beyond the perimeter of the break. The full lamination restored the original thickness in the hull and a bit more.

Considerable suspense and anticipation prevailed when time came to break away the mold. A great deal of work led up to this important point. With the fasteners removed, the mold came free with no fuss. The big patch turned out to be an excellent job. There were no pits or air bubbles and it blended so evenly with the old laminate that a bare minimum of sanding and filling was necessary. The quality of the repair certainly justified the cost and labor involved in fabricating the back-up mold.

Filling and sanding the scratched and gouged areas was a tedious job. The condition was extensive. By this time spring had come and the boat was outside, but the weather was not too cooperative on the weekends.

Deep pits and gouges (over 1/8") were filled up with a mix of chopped glass and polyester resin. A polyester putty worked well for shallow depressions and fairing. This material smooths out and holds well on a vertical surface; it also hardens rapidly so that an efficient work schedule can be maintained. However, the polyester putty was too heavy and viscous for effective use in leveling the scratched portions of the hull. For this condition, Caulkins mixed up a highly filled epoxy resin which was applied in sweeping strokes with a rubber squeegee (photo #23). He made this formulation by adding Santocel filler to a liquid epoxy resin

20   Because of cold weather, "Greyling" was moved to a local garage with central heating,   21
where relaminating of the hole could be efficiently carried out. Alternate layers of
matting and heavy woven roving were applied until the original thickness was reestablished. Plies of glass were staggered and overlapped generously on the sound part of
the hull. Picture at right shows mat being formed in place. Note chain plate strap,
subsequently fastened to new transverse bulkhead.

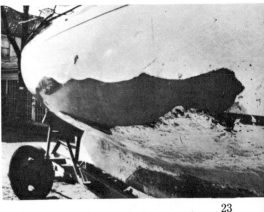

22   Resin is distributed through woven roving and mat with rubber squeegee. Laminating   23
procedure was accomplished in one full day, followed by overnight cure. Removal of
back-up mold (right) revealed an almost perfect patch.

24   Extensive puttying and filling was required to level out the multitude of gouges and   25
scratches in the hull. Two systems proved effective— a filled epoxy resin smeared on
with a rubber squeegee and a polyester resin body compound for relatively deep cuts.
After thorough sanding and application of epoxy paint. "Greyling" appeared as fresh
and new as the day she emerged from her mold.

26 27

New bulkhead section has been fitted to the old portion. Strips of fiberglass used to bond the panel to the shell are shown before impregnation. In bow (right) water tank is partially completed and support framing for the bunks is in place. Note termination of patched area.

until it was of a consistency that would not sag or run when applied to the hull.

It is worthwhile to mention that we found very little necessity for using epoxy resin in this repair project. The epoxy surfacing compound just mentioned turned out to be a good assignment for this product, but it had the annoying disadvantage of taking a long time to cure.

The outside lead ballast had naturally absorbed as much or more abuse as the hull itself, and it too had to be filled and faired out. Because epoxy is better than polyester in adhering to metal, it was used quite exclusively in this area. Due to the heavy pounding, the joint between the keel and "dead wood" had been slightly started; this was carefully filled with epoxy.

The final step, of course, was to paint the entire hull. Two coats of epoxy paint were applied to the topsides and a coat of vinyl anti-fouling to the bottom.

Repairing the large hole in the hull was the heart of this rebuilding project. However, a greater number of work hours went into secondary repairs and modifications which the owner felt necessary.

In the process of cutting away the fractured and delaminated hull shell it was necessary to remove several glassed-in wooden cleats and two bulkheads. Photos #26 and 27 show the new bulkhead section being installed. A layer of four-inch glass mat and tape was used to bond the panel to the relaminated hull shell. In the right-hand corner can be seen the heads of screw bolts which secure the chain plate straps positioned on the other side of the bulkhead.

In the forward compartment can be seen the termination of the patched area and the wood framing which supports the bunks.

Wooden joinery is the customary way of fitting out the interior of a fiberglass hull. Connection between the glass laminate and the wood is

28

Wooden box mold was fabricated to the approximate dimensions of the area to be
added to the skeg (left). Right—Molded piece in place with rudder bearing installed.

Rudder blade featured fiberglass incased wooden core
with solid glass trailing edge.

accomplished in either of two ways. The wooden member, such as this bulkhead, can be laminated directly to the hull, or a wooden cleat may be glassed in and then wood assemblies fastened to this member.

When she pounded on the rocks, **Greyling** lost her rudder and wore away a considerable amount of laminate at the after portion of the skeg. The lower rudder shaft bearing or gudgeon could not be mounted properly without rebuilding the section. The repair technique used here was unique in fiberglass procedure—actually like a wood repair. Because of the awkward position, it was necessary to mold a piece separately and join it to the worn-down portion.

A cut was first made with the saber saw to provide a proper mating surface. Then a simple wood mold was fabricated the dimensions of which approximated the section to be added. (Photos #28 and #29). A solid piece of laminate was laid up in this box mold, using scraps of glass cloth and mat. This piece was then fitted in place with epoxy resin and three stainless machine screws that were properly tapped into the glass deadwood. Mechanical fastenings, in addition to the epoxy bond, may or may not have been necessary. However, this was a critical repair and a point on the bottom of the hull which can be exposed to severe impact.

The machine screws served to clamp the piece in place until the epoxy cured, but they also provided additional security to the joint when tapped and set in epoxy resin.

The original rudder was aluminum. The shaft, tube and miscellaneous components were originally aluminum and stainless steel. Caulkins decided he wanted to build up a fiberglass rudder, and ordered a bronze shaft assembly, a new cuper-nickel tube and bronze lower bearing.

The construction of the rudder blade can be seen quite clearly in Photo #30. The rudder has a wooden core of redwood and white oak. The trailing edge is a tapered piece of solid fiberglass strapped to the main portion of the blade with bronze. The entire assembly is encased in two layers of fiberglass cloth. The redwood serves as a form and filler. Oak was used around the edges and as an insert extending beyond the main straps where extra strength is needed. On the first model, Caulkins tried to carry the oak out in a tapered trailing edge. This proved too weak, however, and it was cut back and the solid fiberglass piece attached in its stead.

The rudder blade is very neat and streamlined, which we believe to be better than the original design. After a season's service, one minor defect resulted. The glass cloth on the upper edge split due to the expansion of the oak strip. This can be readily patched, but it does prove the point that one must be careful about encasing oak in fiberglass. This type of wood exerts a considerable expansion force.

In the process of rebuilding **Greyling**, Caulkins carried out a number of modifications in the interior. The most sizable fiberglass project was the installation of an integral water tank in the bow.

A diagram showing the construction details of the tank accompanies this chapter, but it is worthwhile to go over some of the major features in its construction, as this is the type of fiberglass modification which interests many owners.

Diagram of the integral water tank construction in the bow of a Dolphin. Prefabricated panels were bonded in place with strips of fiberglass mat and tape.

Caulkins decided to eliminate the water tank from a position just forward of the mast support column and build in an integral bow tank beneath the bunks. This space was not readily accessible for any other purpose, and the additional weight forward (20-gallon capacity) did not disturb the design trim of the boat.

The tank was constructed from two basic pieces of prefabricated fiberglass panel—a vertical dam wall and a lid. The pieces bonded to the hull shell with fiberglass mat and woven tape. All fittings were mounted on the panels before installation which reduced the labor of doing this work in the confined area of the hull.

Because fiberglass watertank taste can be a problem, it is worthy to remark that this tank has been quite free of any disagreeable taste. Care was taken that the prefabricated panels were well cured with an infra-red lamp and the tank itself cleaned and flushed thoroughly after assembly.

Miscellaneous Repairs and Alterations

A considerable volume of space existed between the transom and the rudder post, but there was no access. Unlike similar auxiliary designs, the cockpit seats are solid—perhaps intentionally to protect the quarter berths. At any rate, a neat lazarette hatch was cut in the after deck. The opening was made with a saber saw and a mahogany frame and hatch cover of conventional construction was installed. To prevent loose articles in the lazarette from slipping down into the bilge, quarter-inch plywood stops were fiberglassed to the hull shell.

After several heavy rain storms it was discovered that a number of leaks resulted from a poor deck-to-hull connection. In this design the deck was bedded and mechanically fastened to a wooden sheer clamp. The joint was capped with a mahogany toe rail also set in a conventional bedding compound. To remedy the leaks, all the toe rails were removed and a Thiokol-based compound squeezed into the deck-hull joint. Then the rails were re-fastened in gasket of the compound. These new, resilient adhesives are highly recommended over the conventional bedding compounds as they do not dry out and lose their elasticity.

Greyling had no grounding system for protection against lightning. Since it was necessary to strip a good portion of the interior in order to carry out hull repairs, it was an opportune time to do this bonding work. After consultation with Sparkman & Stephens, 3/8" copper tube was selected as the proper conduit. The shrouds, the backstay and the forestay were connectted to a common keel bolt with this tubing. Since the ballast is outside, adequate surface area in direct contact with the water was available.

Summary And Cost Aspects Of Project

Few owners, or boatyards, for that matter, will ever be faced with a fiberglass repair job as large as this one. However, it can be seen from this story that big fractures or holes do not mean that the boat is a total loss.

On the contrary, the basic simplicity in working with fiberglass means that most repairs will require less skill and less time than with conventional boatbuilding materials.

The cost of rebuilding **Greyling** was reasonable, but it is not possible to use this job as an exact standard because so much alteration work was added to the basic repair. Certain specific cost figures and general facts are noteworthy.

Greyling was acquired by Caulkins at a very attractive price, which was the major inducement for him to take on the project. The amount of labor is hard to evaluate (about 20 weekends), but his total actual costs provided him with a boat for approximately one-half her value before she was damaged. And this cost included many modifications and improvements.

We know from studying other repair jobs like this one that the cost of relaminating the structure will be a relatively small per cent of the total. Redoing the interior joiner work, overhauling the engine and the electrical system—these are the time-consuming and costly elements.

The material costs involved in the fiberglass work are interesting and perhaps helpful. The mold form section which came from the factory cost $125. The total fiberglass material cost was about $95, polyester resin (20 gallons) $100. About 25 per cent of the glass and resin went into building the back-up mold, another 25 per cent into building the rudder, water tank and miscellaneous bonding operations. Two quarts of epoxy resin and several cans of polyester putty added another $15. About $60 was spent on special equipment and incidentals—acetone, brushes, heat lamps, saber saw blades, sandpaper, rental of heavy-duty power sander (used in working the fiberglass and resin). The total bill for this important phase of the work, was under $400.

Greyling is now as structually sound as the day she was built. Caulkins or subsequent owners should never have any fears about her. The boat was sailed quite hard at various times since the repair, and in addition, the writer unwittingly gave the repaired area a good test. She went aground on a mud-gravel bank during an outgoing tide and came to rest high and dry on her starboard side. The patched area took some sharp bumps from the wash created by passing boats. I believe such impact would at least have started the seams on a wood-planked hull.

RECONSTRUCTING FIBERGLASS

The "Cheetah" Project

Mrs. Rose M. Booz bought the 26' Chris-Craft Capri hulk for $100. She recounts that the sloop had broken loose from its moorings during a storm. The hull was badly holed and most of the superstructure had been sheared away when swept under the Raritan River Railroad Bridge.

It is an exceptional job of rebuilding. Even with the visual proof of the photographs, it was hard to believe that such a badly fragmented superstructure could have been restored without benefit of a mold. The rebuilt truck has completely fair lines and only close inspection would give any indication that fiberglass repairs had been carried out.

Under ordinary circumstances, the loss of such an extensive area of laminate would be handled in either of two ways. One would be to obtain the entire new deck assembly, or perhaps just the trunk portion, from the boatbuilder. In this case, the Capri design was no longer in production, and the cost of the approach was not attractive to Mr. and Mrs. Booz. A second way would be to make a fiberglass cast or form from another Capri, bolt this mold form to the damaged hull, and proceed to relaminate the structure. This latter technique has been used in hull repair from time to time, but is not terribly practical for a big deck section.

In most instances, fiberglass hulls which have been damaged as badly as this one are never rebuilt. It's just too expensive and troublesome a task for the ordinary boat yard, and too big a project for the average home craftsman. However Mr. and Mrs. Booz had the necessary energy and ingenuity to successfully complete the project.

Materials and methods

Cheetah was reconstructed with a remarkably small inventory of materials and equipment. Mrs. Booz reported that they used about twelve yards of ten-ounce boat cloth, a little loose-chopped fiber, about ten gallons of polyester resin, and a considerable but unspecified amount of polyester auto body putty. She noted that the putty was invaluable in re-establishing fairness and finish.

It is worthwhile to mention that repairs of this type are ordinarily not carried out exclusively with cloth—that a combination of cloth and chopped strand mat and perhaps a ply of woven roving are more commonly selected. Mr. and Mrs. Booz were not familiar with these "in shop" reinforcements though and chose to stay with the fiberglass cloth. The strength and quality of the repair in no way suffered by their choice.

The patient and painstaking way the fragments of the trunk were jigged and clamped together to reproduce the form was certainly a most interesting feature of the project. It should be of some guidance to readers who are interested in the art of fiberglass repair. But possibly the most useful technique displayed was the method of employing foam to reconstruct an area of multiple curvature. Blocks of Styrofoam are readily available and the material can be easily and quickly shaped with a hand tool.

Since the styrene component in the liquid polyester resin acts as a solvent for Styrofoam, causing it to physically "melt," a paint, a plastic film or possibly epoxy resin must be applied to protect the foam. In the case of **Cheetah**, strips of plastic tape were chosen to act as the barrier. It's worth mentioning that rigid polyurethane foam is widely used in fiberglass boat construction for flotation and double-skin hulls and decks. It is not attacked by polyester resin.

How to Regard Heavily Damaged Fiberglass Hulls

There are several general points about fiberglass repairs which are brought to mind by this case history. In the first place, it is clear that the application of the materials can be mastered with very little experience—and a very important supporting point is that mistakes are always correctable. The ability to cut, grind and reshape the laminate eliminates the necessity for absolute precision in preliminary lay-up.

Secondly, the sight of a badly damaged boat like **Cheetah** is sometimes disturbing to people who are not familiar with fiberglass construction. They may be bothered by the relative thinness of the exposed broken structure and a bit aghast at the gaping holes. To begin, one has to appreciate the fact that no small boat of any material is going to do very well in an encounter with a railroad bridge. Something had to give and no one should be surprised that the bridge won by shearing away the trunk. How might a wooden or metal hull have stood up in such a collision? It's a matter of conjecture, but the wreckage would have had a different appearance; people are more familiar with the sight of crumbled and torn metal or crushed and split planking.

Due to its resilient strength, a fiberglass structure will absorb a great deal of force. But since it has no bending or yield point, it either breaks decisively at its load limit or bounces back to its original shape. This characteristic is advantageous in absorbing shock energy and at the same time facilitates repair. The fractures are relatively localized and the broken shell will hold its basic shape within acceptable tolerances.

Regarding the thickness aspect, one cannot automatically equate the strength of the structure with the thickness of the laminate. This is particularly so in the case of Chris-Craft hulls, for a lot of research goes

"Cheetah," in a Raritan salt marsh, after having been swept under a railroad bridge. Her superstructure was almost demolished and her hull badly holed.

into the engineering of the laminate so that a strong, yet light-weight structure is assured. In addition to this, one must recognize that a hull of this type has a monocoque strength integrity. That is, much like aircraft design, it is a unitized structure. Mrs. Booz remarked on this in her own way when she stated that when the pieces were in a loosely assembled form she was skeptical of the strength and rigidity that were finally achieved when the entire trunk unit was laminated together.

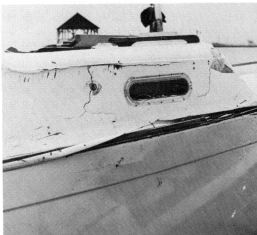

Left: The trunk roof from the forward hatch aft had been completely smashed in. Some pieces remained in the cabin; other fragments littered her resting place. Right: While the forward part of the trunk was badly fractured, the Boozes were able to utilize the form in their relamination procedure.

Left: Many hours were spent in gathering up fragments of the trunk. Like an improbable jigsaw puzzle, big pieces were developed out of small pieces. Right: The trunk in the companionway area begins to take form again. Clamps hold the sections in place and in proper alignment while relamination was carried out.

Left: Starboard corner of the trunk doghouse was remolded, using a shaped block of Styrofoam as a form. A layer of plastic tape prevented the liquid polyester resin from disintegrating the Styrofoam. Right: Portion of the trunk has been bonded together with glass and resin. The lip of the forward hatch is being remolded, using a framework of wood as a form.

Left: Glass cloth and resin reestablished the structure. Polyester body putty was the most important ingredient in filling and fairing out surface irregularities. Right: Another view of the forward hatch remolding and adjacent trunk area. Note the heavy duty disc sander. This tool is a necessity for a project of this magnitude.

Below left: Except for final sanding and painting, the cabin structure has been completely restored. Plywood stiffening panels have been laminated to the underside portion of the top. Below right: Mrs. Booz sands down an application of polyester putty. Dust created by grinding the glass-resin surface can be quite irritating, though not dangerous. A respirator, and loose fitting protective clothing are recommended for extensive projects, especially in enclosed areas.

Above: Finished with several coats of polyurethane paint, the cabin structure is like new. The surface is fair and smooth—virtually no evidence of the complex reconstruction that was carried out. Below: "Cheetah" returns to the water.

CHAPTER 13

Sealants and Adhesives

MODERN CHEMISTRY HAS PRODUCED an extraordinary number of new paints, adhesives, and sealants. Even if you are deeply engaged in an engineering field it is increasingly difficult to be completely current on all the new products and processes. Changes are occurring with great rapidity. The products we will discuss are familiar to the writer. but they do not necessarily represent all the new eligible candidates. Additionally, we consider them primarily in regard to fiberglass hulls although they can also be very useful in the building and maintenance of wood and steel hulls.

For carrying out repairs and modifications to your fiberglass boats there are probably two general classifications of adhesives and sealants which will be required—rigid and flexible. The rigid types will serve for bonding fiberglass to fiberglass, metal to fiberglass, wood to fiberglass and will facilitate laminate repairs. The flexible types are most properly considered for sealing through-hull connections, window or port-light installations; in general, all types of metal-to-fiberglass or wood-to-fiberglass connections where mechanical fasteners are the primary holding method and the synthetic, plastic, serves as a sealant.

Polyester And Epoxy Compounds

These two plastics, as they would best be used around a fiberglass hull, represent what we would call the rigid type adhesive. Since virtually all hulls are molded with a polyester resin, the polyester putties or compounds are naturally compatible.

The practical question which frequently comes up is: "When do you use an epoxy resin and when do you employ the polyester?" About 95 per cent of all molded fiberglass boat repairs can be done with polyester. Using polyester with a scarf joint, for example, the bond will be very strong. There are a few instances, however, where epoxy, because of its superior adhesive characteristics, would be better. Examples would be repair jobs which allow for a very small scarf or overlap, or where a metal member has to be bonded to the laminate.

Where adhesion is clearly a critical factor, the epoxy should be used.

But the point is that very often you do not need all the adhesive value of the epoxy, and the easier handling characteristics of the polyester make it a better choice. Another important point is that unless you get a complete cure with the epoxy resin, the adhesive strength cannot be realized. It might, in fact, be considerably inferior to the polyester counterpart under marginal heat conditions. More often than not, we have to work on our boats out in the open during the spring of the year when cold damp days occur with annoying frequency.

The highly viscose consistency of both the polyester and epoxy compounds is often provided by fine particle fillers of metal, clay, silica or asbestos. Metal fillers seem to be used quite a bit with epoxies. When fillers are properly blended with polyester resins, adhesive properties are improved to a marked degree because inherent shrinkage is reduced.

Epoxy cements are widely available today from hardware and marine supply stores. There are many brand names. Polyester putties are best obtained from automotive supply stores, marine hardware stores, and plastic supply firms. The polyester products have a limited shelf life, and this is probably the reason that many ordinary retail outlets do not stock them.

Polyester Putty

Polyester putty compounds are effective for filling nicks, scratches, and gouges. They contain the same basic polyester resin which is used in the construction of the hull, but differ in that they have a high percentage of inorganic filler which provides the necessary viscosity and helps reduce shrinkage.

The material is of a buttery consistency and handles like a caulking compound. It sets up very hard in a short time. With a heavy dose of catalyst, curing time can be shortened to twenty minutes or so at room temperature. Sanding and fairing operations can be carried out immediately after the materials have solidified. A certain amount of color blending can be done by mixing in color pigments.

Epoxy Putty

Of the same consistency approximately as the polyester putty, epoxy cement commonly comes in tubes or small cans with a two-part, half-and-half mixing procedure required. The material has tremendous adhesive strength and cures to a rock-like hardness. It can fulfill the same duties as the polyester putty, but is by far the best candidate where a strong adhesive bond is required. Typical categories of uses might be: bonding two fiberglass sections together, bonding metal to fiberglass, bonding wood to fiberglass.

Epoxy cements or putties take longer to set up even under optimum conditions. Increasing the percentage of catalyst or curing agent does not quicken the curing time in the same way as the polyester types. Auxiliary heat, perhaps, in the form of an infra-red bulb, is often employed for local applications.

Epoxy Surfacing Compound

This material is essentially of the same type and consistency as the cement adhesive. It is packaged in larger cans suitable for relatively large area applications. It is especially well-formulated for troweling a protective coat on metal centerboards and keels. It would also be an ideal material for fairing out a fiberglass hull or restoring a smooth surface to a badly gouged or scraped bottom.

Epoxy Liquid Resin

When an epoxy resin is to be laminated with fiberglass materials, the viscous, paste-type resins cannot be used. Proper glass saturation is too hard to obtain. The liquid epoxies are, by the same token, too "runny" to use as a repair for gouges and scratches unless they are on a horizontal plane.

While liquid polyester and fiberglass are satisfactory for the repair of most holed or fractured hulls, there may be cases when the extra adhesion of an epoxy would be called for. For instance, if a boat sustained a break at a critical stress point where the repair patch had only a limited area of contact, it would be safer to use an epoxy laminating resin.

Epoxy Flexible Seam Filler

Here is an interesting and useful material which belies the normally rigid characteristics of epoxies. It is perhaps most obviously applicable to planked wooden decks, but would also be suggested for certain places on a fiberglass boat. Flexible seals under deck stanchions or keel-to-hull joints would be examples.

Underwater Epoxy Repairs

There is also an epoxy repair formulation which seems to be a good one. This is an epoxy plastic which will harden underwater (total immersion or in air) and adheres to steel, wood, concrete, etc. As the reader will observe, careful instructions are given about the ordinary polyesters and epoxies being given adequate heat and dryness to effect proper cure. Here is a new chemical advance which eliminates these precautions and allows application under the most adverse circumstances.

Shell Chemical, as a base producer of epoxy resins, has done quite a bit of field experimentation with this system. One of the more interesting uses has been the application to the steel legs of offshore oil rigs. The material is applied in a poultice form by a skin diver.

Flexible Sealants

A profusion of synthetic resilient compounds has generally become available to boatbuilders. Many of the brand or generic names will be recognizable—Thiokol, polyurethane, neoprene, Hypalon, silicone, and so on.

Since wood and metal boats characteristically have many seams and joints, the development of these modern compounds has found more effective use in these forms of construction than fiberglass. However, while areas of water penetration are reduced in a fiberglass hull, the remaining ones are quite important.

In our experience many of the early fiberglass auxiliaries and powerboats developed small annoying leaks at through-hull points. Examples would be keel bolts, deck stanchions, mechanical deck-to-hull joints. And, most common of all, has been leakage around window or port-light frames. The troubles were due to lack of installation care and the relatively poor characteristics of the old bedding compounds which lacked long-term resiliency. With today's new, improved sealants these problems have been largely eliminated.

One of the most popular and useful modern sealants used on fiberglass hulls today is the well-known Thiokol-based material. The material has an epoxy base and is like a "self-vulcanizing" chemical rubber with permanent flexibility. Such sealants are basically immune to the elements and all fuels, chemicals, or acids associated with boat operation. Until recently they have been offered as a two-part system. We now understand that they can be applied without the addition of the catalyst component.

A relatively new "miracle" sealant product is becoming very popular with boat builders and repairers—silicone rubber. Dow Chemical and General Electric are the two biggest producers. The product is now readily available in marine hardware stores.

The silicone rubber is more expensive than the Thiokol-based varieties, but for small jobs it is easier, neater and cleaner to use. It comes in a handy tube with a well-designed injection nozzle. No catalyzation is required. Lower curing temperatures aren't such a problem. The natural color is white rather than the brown and black of Thiokol. The material starts curing when exposed to the air and sets up to a tenacious, rubbery consistency in a few hours. If you have a window-leak problem, silicone rubber is a marvelous remedy.

We know about, but are not properly familiar with, other elastomeric sealant products which are being used in the marine field. Examples would be the polyurethane and various types of synthetic rubber. Eliminating these products from our discussion does not imply that they are unsuitable. We do suggest experimentation for evaluation. It is certain that for a number of years to come the boat owner is going to be offered many different chemical products to use on his boat, and it will behoove him to be receptive and to use the "acid" test—try them.

CHAPTER 14

Maintenance

THE INTEGRAL MOLDED FINISH on fiberglass hulls has proved to be a very advantageous feature. Ostensibly, the need for painting and associated rituals is done away with. But is this actually and literally true? Today's fiberglass boat owner will acknowledge the virtues of the "molded in" finish but he knows it is not maintenance-free. For example, antifouling bottom paints are required for protection, but may be needed after a period of years for appearance's sake. No color pigments are completely permanent, they will eventually fade and deteriorate from the ultraviolet rays of the sun. Also, any boat will accumulate scratches and surface mars.

All such factors considered, a balanced appraisal indicates that seasonal or regular periodic painting and refinishing is not required—the need for such procedure depends on the type of service, exposure and general care given the hull. Regarding the latter point, it is generally agreed from experience today that regular washdown and protective waxing can be very beneficial to preserving and protecting the original "factory" finish on fiberglass hulls.

Particularly in years past, the finish on glass hulls has been the subject of a degree of controversy with regard to maintenance and expected durability. Some of the criticism leveled has been rightfully supported by a relatively small amount of poor product performance. The larger part of the problem has been due to misunderstanding about how to care for the hull finish. It's probably true that any new material of this nature must undergo a "consumer familiarization" phase.

In this section we will investigate certain types of surface "cosmetic" problems which have occurred in glass hulls. We will try to accurately explain the cause and suggest general repair techniques that have proved successful. It is doubtful whether any glass boat owner has experienced all these troubles and more than likely that many owners have never been aware that such defects exist. With today's glass hull, these surface defects are not often encountered.

The nature of the gel coat

The smooth, colored exterior finish on almost all fiberglass hulls is provided by a thick (about 15 mils) layer of resin which is permanently fused to the laminate shell in the molding process. This so-called gel coat

Good coat of wax at least once a year and periodic washdowns will add years of life to high-gloss finish.

is not reinforced with glass as the fibers would be quite apparent and detract from appearance. Since the boats are generally laid up in a female mold, application of the gel coat is the first step. It may be applied with a brush, but more often with a spray gun.

Because of weathering and general wear and tear, the gel coat has very demanding performance requirements. By comparison, the glossy finish on an automobile or kitchen appliance is rarely exposed to the abuse which the average boat hull receives.

This surface resin layer must be hard enough to resist scratching and abrasion but elastic and resilient enough to absorb impact without crracking. The resin of necessity is formulated with a greater elongation property than the glass reinforced laminate shell. To preserve the color pigment and resist chalking, special additives are incorporated to absorb destructive ultraviolet rays of the sun.

The life of a gel coat

Just how long a gel coat will stand up cannot be answered in definite terms. It depends on the type of exposure and care given the hull. Florida sun, for instance, will fade colors many times faster than that in the northern sun. The acceptability of appearance will, of course, vary from one owner to another.

Certain colors look better for a longer period of time. White, although it is not a color, can give six or eight years service if cared for properly. Beige colors, light gray and light blue seem to stand up better than dark colors. Fading is not necessarily objectionable if it is uniform and not a drastic change.

The commonly available household detergents and mild abrasive kitchen cleansers will take care of the average layer of dirt and grime. Stubborn scuff marks can be removed with a soaped steelwool scouring pad, but use of these pads must be reserved because they will dull a high gloss gel coat after repeated use. In addition, all the tiny steel-wool particles must be flushed away or they will shortly cause a rust stain. Heavy deposits of oil or grease can be wiped off with special cleaners, benzine, gasoline, or kerosene without harming the plastic. Stubborn marks of tar or grease may become a problem if wedged in a badly molded pattern, but ordinarily a deck brush and kerosene or gasoline will dissolve such residue.

The finish on the fiberglass boat is similar in character to that of an automobile and will respond to the same system of care and cleaning. Car waxers and cleaners are often used on fiberglass boats to maintain a sparkling finish. A variety of polishes and cleaners for fiberglass are now on the market. Some are very good and we suggest experimenting with several brands to determine what you like best. These products appear to fall into two categories—a polish cleaner (similar to the auto type) and a fine abrasive cleaner.

Waxing the topsides on fiberglass hulls works the same way as on automobiles. The wax film keeps the surface from soiling, makes it easier to wash and definitely extends the service life of the gel coat. Waxing and polishing of the deck surface and superstructure is perhaps an optional matter, as many owners have discovered that it reduces traction and increases glare.

If the plastic finish has degraded to the point that there is considerable fading and perhaps a chalky film condition, one of the newer "heavy-duty" fiberglass boat cleaners should be tried. When followed with a wax polish the original gloss comes back quite satisfactorily. Such a product is now widely distributed by the Du Pont Co. Its nature and action are very similar to the fine-grain rubbing compounds used to bring back the finish on heavily oxidized aluminum.

TO PAINT OR NOT TO PAINT

When to paint above the waterline

Since so many factors influence the life of pigmented gel coat, it is not possible to predict its longevity with accuracy. We know that ten-year performance is certainly not uncommon, but perhaps four to six years is more generally representative. When cleaners and polishes will no longer brighten the finish acceptably, eliminating scratches and mars, then a paint system has to be employed. As yet, reapplication of gel coats and color matching of an extensive nature are not a very practical answer for the owner, or for the average boatyard. In fact, such procedures can well be costly and time-consuming when compared to modern paint systems.

Once the decision to paint has been made with a fiberglass hull, it does not mean a seasonal commitment. Properly applied, paint stands up well on a fiberglass surface. Unlike wood and metal, the fiberglass laminate is stable, nonpourous and not subject to underfilm corrosion or deterioration.

What type of paint to use

In the last few years the marine paint companies have come out with a profusion of new formulations, many of which are derived from advances in coatings and adhesive chemistry. Brand identity with such "miracle" products as polyurethane, epoxy, silicone and acrylic are common. The situation is perhaps confusing, but a good selection can result from a certain amount of basic understanding and ordinary common sense.

Experience with these various types of paints seems to point out that the care and thoroughness with the way they are applied is the most important consideration. In other words, the actual performances of these new paints all seem to live up quite well to their claims if preparation and application instructions are followed closely.

Boatyards and individual owners usually settle on one type of paint system or another as much for ease of application as for confidence and satisfaction in the end result. Since most boats today are still painted out-of-doors or, at best, under relatively uncontrolled conditions, paint products which are quite sensitive to temperature, humidity and fussy mixing procedures have limited popularity. A few words on the principal characteristics of these modern yacht paints is offered here as a guide.

Epoxy paints have been around for some time now, introduced at a time when fiberglass hulls were becoming popular. Their excellent adhesion and hardness is well matched to the requirements of fiberglass and metal surfaces. However, epoxy paints have not provided a universal answer. They are prone to chalking and lack color retention, although periodic cleaning and waxing will help a great deal. Two-part chemical mixing procedures of many types detract from their appeal.

Alkyd-base paints are the old standby of the yacht industry and have not been displaced. Modern formulations are improved. They have good color and gloss retention, brush on smoothly and evenly. The film thickness is heavier than, say, an epoxy and not as hard. But the all-round performance and ease of application keeps them in demand.

Polyurethanes have unique elastic toughness, color retention and chalk resistance. Popular for clear coatings such as varnish, they are more often offered as blends in paint formulations. This apparently is due to the tricky problems of applying polyurethanes in a pure form.

Acrylics have proven to be best in outdoor weathering, long-term gloss and color retention. For marine paints, they are incorporated into blends.

Need for bottom paint

Whether in salt water or fresh, a glass hull needs antifouling protection. Marine organism will not penetrate or otherwise damage the material, but grass, barnacles and other growths will cling as tenaciously and grow as luxuriantly as on any other hull material. Any antifouling paint can be used on a glass hull. The main concern is that the surface be prepared properly so that good adhesion is obtained. This factor is also important on areas above the waterline, but it is much more critical on the bottom.

Surface preparation is important

Professionals in the marine paint business and those in boat repair work feel that most paint failures or disappointments are due to improper surface preparation and/or poor mixing and application technique. This has been almost a demonstrated fact since paints were first used, and it applies more strongly than ever now. The fiberglass laminate is smooth, hard and nonporous. Getting good paint adhesion to it, compared with a wooden hull, has proven more difficult. Procedures which may be adequate for wood boats (particularly below the waterline) can prove to be entirely inadequate for glass. Peeling and blistering are two common symptoms of adhesive failure.

The greatest incidence of problems concerns bottom paints—for several reasons. In the first place, a major contributor to poor paint bonding results from the residual wax mold release agent that is on the gel coat surface of virtually every new fiberglass boat. Since the molded hull above the waterline will usually not be painted for some years, this wax wears away in time from normal use. Of course, protective waxing of the topsides may build up a film also, but it does not appear to be so critical or difficult to remove. Bottom paints in general do not have high adhesive qualities. Under constant water immersion they eventually suffer from permeability. This sets the stage for trouble if good surface preparation procedures are not carried out.

Fiberglass boatbuilders and paint companies have been diligently trying to perfect a foolproof surface preparation system for years. The fact that there are still a number of products and procedures being recommended suggests that the optimum has not been found. In fact, a quick scan of instructive literature is a bit confusing. Closer study reveals some common rules.

The first objective is to rid the surface of the waxy release agent. How to do this thoroughly and effectively is a matter of some choice. Paint companies have now come out with a variety of "dewaxing" agents or solvents. Since the wax is essentially invisible, it is important to do more than simply redistribute the film by too economic use of rags and cleaner. A good washing with kitchen detergent followed by a fresh water rinse is also recommended to completely neutralize and clean the surface.

At this point, certain paint company instructions say that you can proceed directly with the bottom paint, although some feel a primer is necessary—generally of the epoxy type. Other instructions recommend sanding after the solvent wipe and neutralizing wash.

While solvent "dewaxers" may eliminate the tedious step of sanding, one can't go wrong by adhering to the sanding procedure. There is a time-honored reason for this. A thorough scouring of the surface increases the paint bonding area manyfold. As some say, it gives "tooth" to the smooth surface.

Painting old fiberglass surfaces

The surface preparation principles just discussed also apply here. The initial step would obviously entail a thorough detergent wash to eliminate scum and dirt. The solvent wash would then be recommended if there were any possibility of protective wax build-up. If not, a good sanding and a primer-surfacer would be suggested. If there are scratches and gouges to be filled, this should be done with a polyester putty after cleaning and before priming.

With older fiberglass hulls that have already been painted, do not reapply a fresh coat without first making sure that the existing paint is well adhered and sanded smooth. Also make sure that the new paint will be compatible with old; if uncertain, work a test area first.

Paint removers on fiberglass?

The simplest and best advice here is to confine their usage to below the waterline. The reasons are quite practical.

Removers will attack the gel coat to varying degrees, depending on their strength and how long the solution is left to react. The only need for paint removers is to strip a "paint-sick" condition and this most obviously occurs with an accumulation of seasonal applications of bottom paint. However, old bottom paints yield pretty well to coarse grit paper on an electric sander, so the real utility of chemical paint removers is somewhat debatable.

If you choose to work with a paint remover, try some test areas first so that its strength and effectiveness can be evaluated. Leave the solution on only long enough for it to perform its function and then wipe off with old rags. Completely wash and neutralize the surface after the job is completed, or if the operation is interrupted for any length of time.

A special bottom paint problem

There is at least one chronic and annoying fiberglass bottom paint problem which keeps recurring, irrespective of how carefully the previous procedures have been followed. This has to do with small, pimple-sized paint blisters which occur in the boot-top area and below the waterline (salt or fresh water exposure). The problem has been around for quite a while and generates a lot of earnest inquiries, particularly from sailing skippers.

We have tried over a number of years to determine the real cause for the pimples and, more important, to find out the best remedy. To date the writer simply has an unproven theory on the cause, and a reasonably effective suggestion on the "fix." On the theory end of it, it is believed that the cause may be due to a hydrolysis reaction of slightly undercured gel coat with entrapped solvents; that is, water penetrates the bottom paint, reacts with the gel and gasifies to make a bubble. To support this theory, it is well known that a really improperly cured gel coat is very subject to water attack and will eventually develop deep blisters and cracks.

If the pimple problem is not too extensive, many owners simply live with the condition and sand and repaint when the hull is next hauled. The rash may very well disappear after the second painting.

However, if the condition is extensive and chronic, other corrective steps must be sought. A barrier coat of some sort should be applied over the gel coat—one with good adhesion.and high water resistance. A filled epoxy resin is considered a good selection. Catalyzed epoxy undercoat has been used successfully sometimes, but too often it lacks the necessary body and film thickness.

Gel coat defects and their cause

The accompanying drawings show some of the typical defects. (The drawings tend to highlight the cracks in a more alarming way than really occurs. Most hairline cracks are generally not visible from any appreciable distance.) Six defect examples are shown, five of which indicate gel coat failure due to improper formulation or application.

Crazing can be caused by excessive thickness, too rigid a formulation, or an incompletely cured gel coat which has been prematurely exposed to water. A combination of all three factors can cause the failure of the entire gel coat on a hull, but cases have been very rare.

FIG. 1 shows crazing radiating from the base of a winch pedestal. The cause here might be too rigid or thick a gel coat. The heavy local strains on the winch thus helps induce the surface cracks.

FIG. 2, a cross section of cabin-to-deck area, attempts to show that angles or abrupt changes of plane are beginning points for crazes if the gel coat is too rigid or thick.

FIG. 5 demonstrates a condition where crazing below the waterline has begun to extend through the boot-top area and up the sides. Such a situation is a good indication of lack of proper cure to the resin before it has left the shop. Water, salt or fresh, can attack or hydrolize improperly cured resin. While this statement may have alarming implications, long experience with glass hulls has shown that the reinforced portion of the hull shell has never been structurally degraded by this action, only the thin exterior gel coat is in need of attention.

FIG. 4 illustrates a defect which is also caused by undercured gel coat. For want of a better term, we call them "pocket" blisters. They appear

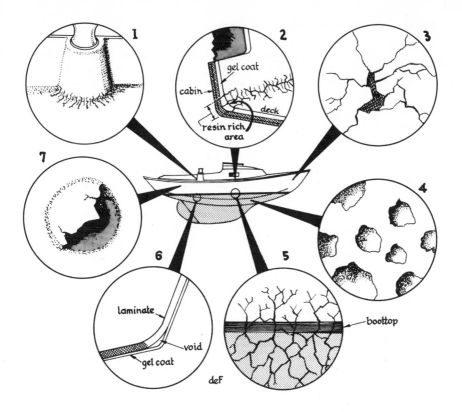

1. Crazing at base of winch pedestal; 2. Crazing at juncture of trunk side and deck; 3. Gel coat damage from severe impact; 4. Small pocket blisters below waterline; 5. Crazing below and above waterline; 6. Void inside gel coat at hard chine; 7. Air bubble behind gel coat in flat area.

below the waterline as a rash, localized or extensive, generally no more than 1/8″ in diameter. Sometimes they break open in small, half-moon fissures, pushing the bottom paint outward until it flakes off. At first it was thought that the cause was a chemical interaction between the metallic ingredients of antifouling paint and resin constituents. This is to some extent true, but primary cause is incompletely cured resin which degrades in small pockets, gas and fluid being forced to the surface.

FIG 6 and 7 concern blisters or voids which may occur during the hull lay-up process. If any turn up at all, they are usually random in nature and widely spaced. FIG. 7 shows a round airbubble variety on a flat area, which might be the size of a dime or quarter. FIG. 6 shows a void at a hard chine where the glass reinforcement has bridged the radius. The existence of such surface bubbles or voids will never be evident until the unsupported, eggshell-like gel coat is crushed. Of course, tapping a suspect area with a metal instrument will readily reveal their existence.

Gel coat repair below the waterline

Since most fiberglass hulls have their bottoms painted, the problem of matching color and finish are not present when making repairs below the waterline. If crazes or blisters are local, they are relatively quick and simple to fix.

Fine crazing on the bottom of the hull can be virtually ignored if the bottom paint will bridge the fissures to give a smooth surface. If the cracks are coarse and open, an epoxy surfacing compound or polyester putty can be worked into the cracks with a squeegee or putty knife.

Whether the crazes or pocket blisters will reoccur after the above treatment is a matter to consider. Practically speaking, by the time the owner has decided that it is necessary to fill the defects, the condition has stabilized and will not extend except at a very slow rate. However, we have seen pocket blisters which have reoccurred after local patching. The effective remedy has been a thorough sanding, filling of the voids, then application of epoxy resin or paste over the entire underbody to seal the surface.

Gel coat repair above the waterline

Patching the gel coat of the topsides and deck is complicated by the problem of matching color and blending in with the customary high-gloss finish. If the defect is a small blister or gouge, the task is not too difficult and can be readily accomplished by the owner. If some local crazing is involved, as for example the condition seen in FIG. 1, the owner should be able to carry out an acceptable repair. If crazing exists over large areas of the topsides or deck, it is simply not practical to patch in the manner prescribed below and the whole area must be resurfaced and painted. Boats with defective gel coats have occasionally had a completely new polyester surface coat applied by spray gun. This is a job to be done in a yard by skilled workmen under controlled conditions. It is an expensive and tedious procedure if a whole hull or deck is involved.

To correct a cobweb or hairline crack, it is first necessary to open it up by making a V-cut with a powered abrasive tool. The cut should extend down and slightly into the laminate and a quarter-inch or so beyond the termination of the hairline fissure. Matching gel coat paste obtained from the boat builder is catalyzed and spread into the V-cut with a spatula. Since the colored gel coat will not set up when exposed to air, a piece of cellophane is spread over the patch and held in place with masking tape. An infrared lamp is effective in implementing the cure when the temperature is below, say 60°. Do not let the lamp get too close.

After 15 or 20 minutes the patch will be partially cured to a sort of rubbery consistency. At this point, the cellophane can be peeled back and trimming or leveling accomplished with razor blade or sharp putty knife. Replace the film and allow the patch to harden. Finish the repair by sanding the area with 600-grit wet sandpaper and fine rubbing compound to bring out the gloss.

Some color difference is bound to be noticed between the old and

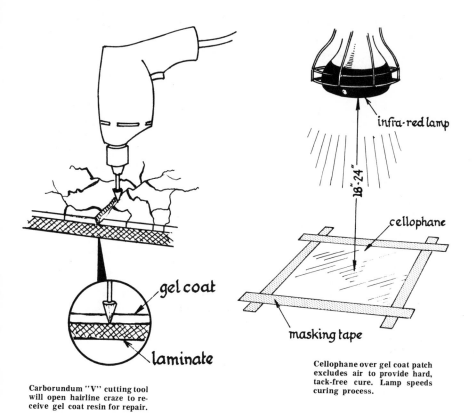

gel coat

laminate

infra-red lamp

18"-24"

cellophane

masking tape

Carborundum "V" cutting tool will open hairline craze to receive gel coat resin for repair.

Cellophane over gel coat patch excludes air to provide hard, tack-free cure. Lamp speeds curing process.

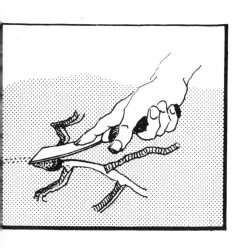

Putty knife and rubber squeegy are useful tools for working resin putty or gel coat into cracks.

new surface, but it is surprising how the patched area will blend in after a few months of weathering.

Can you match color?

Automobile paint shops can match color with great accuracy. This ability has not been developed by the fiberglass boat manufacturers outside their own facilities. It is doubtful whether an owner can do a good matching job. He must use the original pigment paste as it comes from the builder and test to see whether the contrast is within the bounds of acceptability. The size and location of the patch, plus weathering effect will determine resultant appearance.

Scratches

Dark colors, particularly as seen on topsides, show scratches much more clearly than white and other light colors. This is one good reason for selecting the latter.

A repair method for scratches cannot be guaranteed, but the owner should first try vigorous rubbing with a cleaner polish. If unsuccessful, resort to a body rubbing compound. Fine wet paper would be the next choice; use the least abrasive material that will eliminate the scratches. Powered buffing pads should be used with care as they tend to turn at high speed and create excessive heat.

Stains

Stains can occur around the waterline from excessively polluted water or possibly in other locations from rust. Polishes and mildy abrasive compounds should be tried first. In addition, effective stain removers are now on the market. A product called "Rid-O-Rust" is one which has been recommended to us. Presumably these removers contain a bleach-acid solution. It would be wise to experiment with the action of such removers to see whether they will harm finish or color.

COUNTERACTING CONDENSATION

A number of owners of fiberglass cruising boats have been concerned regarding a condensation problem on the interior of their hulls. In a study of the problem we have come up with some facts and corrective agents.

It appears that a fiberglass hull is more prone to sweating than a wooden one. This is due to the density of the fiberglass laminate and the relatively thin cross section. Fiberglass, however, is a far better insulator than either steel or aluminum.

Not all fiberglass boat owners have been bothered with a condensation problem, as there are a number of variables and conditions which influence the occurrence of condensation. Since it occurs from warm, moist air on the inside of the boat coming in contact with cooler hull surface, water temperature is a major factor. In our experience, we have only heard complaints about sweating in northern waters during the summer and in temperate zones during the early spring.

The type and construction of the craft will have a lot to do with the severity of the problem. The fact that fiberglass power cruisers do not seem to sweat very much is probably due to a combination of reasons: relatively large, enclosed air space; high percentage of exterior surface above the water; and the benefit of convected heat from the engines. On the other hand, auxiliaries appear to be the type of fiberglass craft where sweating shows up to be a problem.

One summer, during a cruise off the coast of Maine and Canada, in a 38′ glass yawl, we noted severe condensation at times on the hull surfaces in an unventilated lazarette area and in the main cabin behind the bunks. Beneath the fiberglass decks droplets accumulated, but not as much as on the hull. The cabin trunk was of wooden construction, and there was little or no moisture on ceiling surfaces. The amount of condensation, of course, varied with the atmospheric conditions, inside humidity, efficiency of ventilation, etc., but there was no question that the extremely cold temperature of the water was the major cause.

The type of construction used in the boat will also have a bearing on condensation. For example, many decks and cabin tops are of sandwich construction—perhaps a balsa core with fiberglass skins or some light, synthetic core material. This provides ideal insulating properties. Condensation will not occur on the inside surface once the ceiling is warmed to cabin temperature. Few if any hulls are built with a double skin, but paneling or sheathing the living quarters will isolate the dampness and prevent direct contact with the moisture droplets.

Because condensation is not a common condition, it is doubtful whether builders of stock fiberglass auxiliaries will go to the trouble of making the hull sweat-proof. Therefore, the ideas advanced here are suggestions for the owner to follow in reducing the problem if it appears necessary.

Insulating a fiberglass hull surface is somewhat simplified over wooden and metal construction in that if moisture occurs behind the insulator, rot or corrosion will not take place. This factor does broaden the selection of insulating materials., but you do have the consideration of how to hold the insulating material in place. Adhesive methods seem to be best and the most practical.

While there are undoubtedly many types of anti-sweat sheathings which could be employed, we have investigated two materials that appear to be simple to install, are not costly, and are effective.

Commercial Undercoatings

There are a number of firms throughout the country who specialize in furnishing compounds to undercoat cars, trucks, and similar types of machinery. These thick coatings protect against rust and deaden body noise. The Mortell Co. in Kankakee, Ill., for instance, produces asphaltic and latex compounds which can be brushed, troweled or sprayed on metal surfaces, and are designed to stop condensation on metal surfaces as well as perform the other, above-mentioned functions. These two compounds adhere nicely to a fiberglass laminate. A 1/8″ layer of this material will take care of most sweating problems. The latex type is white and attractive. The asphalt type is black, but does not smudge when rubbed against. The finished surface is "stucco" in appearance. Perhaps this type of surface is not smooth enough for cabin areas, but certainly would be proper in many other locations. We understand that either of these Mortell coatings can be painted.

Foam Padding

When the above type coating may not be suitable, the owner should consider some of the new foam-backed vinyl padding or fabrics. A number of fiberglass boat manufacturers use this material on their interiors. As an example, the Bertram and Hatteras powerboats make use of foam-backed vinyl to line the hull of the forepeak section. This type of installation enhances the appearance and living comfort of the area and will also appreciably deaden sound transmission. The material is naturally a good insulator and will stop condensation. It is felt that approximately a 3/16″ vinyl-faced foam padding should be effective in preventing condensation. The material is usually applied with a pressure sensitive adhesive. Foam fabrics can be obtained from many sources. One product we are familiar with is called Plyhide and is manufactured by Plymouth Rubber Co., of Canton, Mass.

CHAPTER 15

Winter Layup of Fiberglass Boats

LAYING UP A FIBERGLASS BOAT at the end of the boating season is essentially a simple procedure. But there are certain items which should be given proper attention. The points raised are largely confined to the molded fiberglass structure.

Cleanup

Boats which have lain at a mooring all season and are hauled for the winter need a thorough bottom scrubbing. This is best done immediately after hauling. Even if an anti-fouling paint has been used, it is likely that a film of scum has built up. This film is not easy to remove if allowed to dry. If any barnacles have fixed themselves to the bottom, knock them off with a scraper and use a little sandpaper to rid the surface of the hard shell which may still hold fast. Barnacles seem to fuse tightly to a fiberglass surface which has not been protected by anti-fouling paint. They won't damage the fiberglass hull, but are a nuisance.

Algae or scum, which will not come free in the washing procedure, is easily removed with steel wool pads (use the finer grades). Scouring pads such as SOS are very effective. Fiberglass hulls which have been in dirty water for an extended period may show stain on an unpainted bottom and perhaps to a few inches above the waterline. It is naturally most visible on a white hull. A fine steel wool pad dusted with a kitchen cleanser will do the job in most cases. However, if this treatment does not yield satisfactory results, the owner will have to consider paint on the bottom and a painted boot top to restore the desired appearance to the topsides.

Washing down the topsides, deck, and interior is an optional procedure, but if the boat is to be covered all winter, such care in the fall will reduce the work in the spring. Also, deposits of oil, grease or dirt, which are hard to clean while the boat is in the water, will only attract more residue while laid up.

Proper Shoring Or Cradle Supports

As in the case of boats built of other materials, it is important that fiberglass hulls be supported properly when stored on land. Although the strength and monocoque integrity of a fiberglass hull will make it highly resistant to strain and distortion, it is possible to injure the structure if very poor procedures are used. One should follow the traditional systems of support employed for wooden craft.

Winter Covers

The colored surface coat on a fiberglass boat will last many times longer if it is cared for and protected. For this reason either inside storage or a winter cover are highly desirable. In actual fact the intense rays of the summer sun take a greater toll on the plastic gel coat than the weak winter light. Nonetheless, adequate protection from winter weather is greatly beneficial to the long-term appearance of the boat. Larger craft should have a loose-fitting cover that protects the deck and superstructure and, since most sizable fiberglass boats have some wooden exterior or interior components, the usual provisions against water and dampness are important. Mildew may accumulate on fiberglass surfaces, but will not cause damage and can be wiped away.

A small fiberglass boat (i.e., dinghy, small day sailer or outboard) which can readily be turned upside down doesn't need a protective cover. However, to the degree that the fine finish can be minutely eroded and etched by exposure to the elements, a simple plastic cover or canvas tarp will protect the original glossy finish.

Drain Bilges, Water Tanks, Check Air Tanks

Ice resulting from frozen water accumulation in various parts of a fiberglass boat will not cause damage under normal conditions. Because the material will not absorb moisture and because it has a high degree of resilience, ice (except in considerable volume and under the most confining circumstances) will not cause injury.

By way of example, we have allowed a sailing dinghy to remain inverted and uncovered every winter. The centerboard trunk is a closed unit. Water remains in it all winter long, freezing and thawing. The trunk has been exposed for seven winters without injury to the fiberglass laminate.

However resistant the material is to such pressures, common sense precautions are best observed. Undoubtedly a full fiberglass water tank can expand to the rupture point if the contents become a solid, frozen mass. Such tanks should be drained, and bilges should be kept dry. Air chambers (flotation compartments) ought to be checked to see that water has not accumulated from condensation or as a result of a small pinhole.

With regard to fiberglass fuel tanks, most people prefer to top them off; i.e., leave the tank full so that moisture vapor will not condense and settle as free water in the bottom of the tank. Contamination from rust, corrosion, or gumming is not a problem with fiberglass fuel tanks. The need for clean-out should occur only if water, dirt, or other substances have accumulated.

Wet Storage and Operation In Freezing Climates

Wet storage of fiberglass boats in a northern climate is relatively practical. The material will resist damage more than wood and, compared to metals, there will be no danger of corrosion. The laminate has a slick, hard surface very resistant to the cutting action of ice.

By example, we can point to the practice of sheathing wooden with fiberglass to protect them from razor-sharp skim ice. Molded fiberglass duck boats have been used successfully for years in Wisconsin and Minnesota lakes that often freeze over early in the hunting season.

A molded boat, because of its impact resistance and resiliency, will break through thick ice without any damage. Generally the determining factor is whether the engine has power enough to push through the ice formation. Surface scratches may occur to the plastic finish after repeated contact with sharp ice, but we have been surprised how minor are the effects. The plastic surface is very slippery and the hull yields and releases itself quite readily.

Where ice thickness is not great (say over four-inches) and violent movement and pressures are not involved, it may be entirely practical to consider wet storage of a fiberglass boat. The abrasive and cutting action at the waterline may certainly mar the outer coat of resin slightly, but this can be greatly reduced by the traditional method of surrounding the hull with a cordon of sapling branches.

Fiberglass And Cold Temperatures

It is worthwhile to repeat that fiberglass-plastic boats are not adversely affected by cold temperatures. As a matter of fact, some significant increase in laminate strength is noted as very cold temperatures are approached. Special refrigeration containers of fiberglass-plastic construction sustain their contents at temperatures of minus 200° F. Fiberglass boats and other pieces of molded fiberglass equipment have been used repeatedly in arctic expeditions. Certain plastics (generally those of the thermo-plastic variety) do become quite brittle under cold conditions, but the polyester (and in rare cases epoxy type resins) which bonds the glass fibers does not suffer reduction of strength.

The fiberglass boat owner should not be concerned about even the severest winter conditions if he has used reasonable care in the laying up of his craft. The basic material is unaffected by atmospheric temperature extremes. It will not absorb moisture, swell, shrink or distort in any way. Protective measures suggested have more to do with preserving the original finish and appearance than avoiding any real deterioration.

Check Before Launching

All points of stress and vibration on the hull or deck structure should be looked over. In outboard boats, assemblies such as seats and windshields, which are mechanically fastened, may have been loosened by severe pounding. In some boats, thwarts or broken brackets may be of value to the structural integrity of the hull, so it is important that these members be securely fastened.

In this day of massive outboard horsepower, with resultant high speed and impact, the careful owner will give his rig a thorough annual check to see that the structure is sound. Good fiberglass construction offers maximum security, but it just makes good sense to conduct a visual, routine check to see whether, by poor design or overloading, weaknesses have developed.

Having examined many boats over a period of years, we have seen somewhat of a pattern to the difficulties which occasionally arise. First of all, unless a fiberglass hull is involved in an accident, a rupture of the hull shell is very unlikely. Of course, if the boat was very poorly constructed, or if it was stressed beyond reason this could occur but, because of the elasticity and resultant impact strength of the laminate, such instances are rare. What normally involves trouble then is a panel deflection that terminates at some stiffening member or joint. More simply said, look for stress cracks at bond joints or where some fiberglass connection is made. Examples might be the bond between longitudinal stiffener and hull shell, termination of double bottom floor and hull shell, thwart or bulkhead and hull shell.

If the owner finds definite evidence of failure at a joint or connection, it is easily repaired with a piece of fiberglass cloth and epoxy or polyester resin.

Before concluding these comments on structural survey, I'd like to offer a suggestion on a practical test technique which I have employed on a number of occasions. Several years ago we built a test hull utilizing a special type of fiberglass flat-sheet laminate. In the course of evaluating the boat, she was allowed to pound very severely on a rocky bottom. This resulted in a multitude of slow, weeping leaks. After hauling the boat, steps were taken to repair the damage. It turned out that the small breaks or lesions were difficult to locate, for the elastic nature of the material tended to close up the breaks. After some consideration we ended up by using a strong light, x-ray fashion, to spot the breaks in the shell. By shining a bright light on the outside of the hull, close to the shell, we were able to see from the inside just where the difficulties lay. Even a heavily pigmented laminate will transmit light to a degree, and if the boat rests in a shaded or darkened location it is surprising what can be observed.

This idea is not new. Many of the fiberglass boats for the government, particularly prototypes, are built without color pigment or paint so that the quality of the laminate can be visually judged by an inspector.

It goes without saying that such a single test technique does not divulge all physical properties of a laminate, but it is a useful technique to determine the extent of rupture or damage which can sometimes be concealed.

CHAPTER 16

Repairing Wood With Fiberglass

A HOLED PLYWOOD BOAT can be repaired very effectively with fiberglass materials. The fiberglass system is easy and quick since less precision and skill are necessary than when using conventional woodworking techniques. The accompanying photographs show how a badly damaged Highlander sloop was restored with fiberglass and resin materials. The molded-plywood hull had been holed in a number of places on a rocky shore after going adrift from her mooring during a storm.

The principles of the repair system described can be applied to any sheet or molded-plywood structure. Also, it is interesting to note that the procedure is virtually identical with that employed in repairing a punctured molded fiberglass hull.

Materials To Use

Two types of fiberglass reinforcement can be used for the job: fiberglass boat fabric (about 10-oz. per square yard, plain open weave) and fiberglass chopped-strand mat (1 oz. or 1½ oz. per square foot). Boat

Larry Kean

The bottom of the molded plywood hull presented a discouraging sight. She was gouged and holed many times over her entire length (there were more than twelve breaks varying from one inch to over 12" in diameter). It is interesting to note that although damaged so extensively the hull form remained true.

Photos by Larry Kean

A saber saw was used to cut away the splintered edges back to the sound portion of the wood.

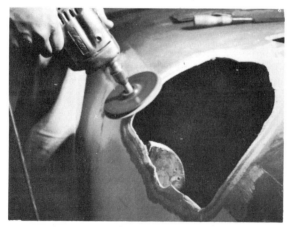

A coarse disc sander (4-16 grit) was used to scarf the edge of the hole. A two-inch scarf joint would be minimum for any hole this large. Three inches would be better. The owner elected to build the patch on the exterior as fairing up the convex surface presented an easier job.

A back-up plate of cardboard, held in place with vattens and tape, was placed on the inside of the hull behind the hole. Thin sheet aluminum or similar formable material could also serve the same purpose. Paste wax should be applied to the back up material so that the cardboard or metal can readily be stripped from the patch after cure.

156

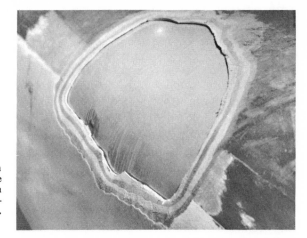

The scarfed hole as seen from the outside with the cardboard back-up plate in place is now ready to receive the fiberglass patch.

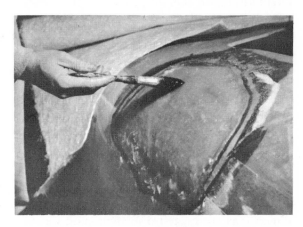

Alternate layers of fiberglass mat and cloth impregnated with resin were applied until the original thickness of the hull was reestablished. Mat builds up thickness rapidly and forms readily to sharp radii. Cloth has high tensile strength, wets and handles easily. Its exclusive use is recommended where an epoxy resin is employed because of the resin's high viscosity. The procedure here might also be done in reverse—that is, scarfing from the inside of the hull and forming the back-up plate to the exterior.

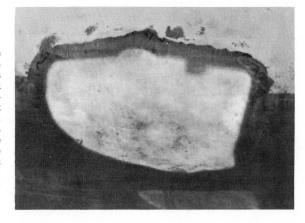

The structural part of the patching has been accomplished and the surface has been ground down so that it fairs in smoothly and evenly with the hull proper. It will be noticed that the patch is quite translucent. It is permissible to allow the patch to cure before the buildup is completed, but the hardened surface should be rough-sanded before adding new material.

fabric is readily available from almost any marine supply source. The mat usually is offered in fiberglass repair kits or can be obtained from a local fiberglass distributor or a fiberglass boat manufacturer. The resin can be either polyester or epoxy type. In repairing the molded-plywood Highlander, polyester was used, but we prefer epoxy resin when applying local patches on wooden hulls because of its superior adhesion.

Dry Wood Surface Necessary

The resin will not bond dependably if the wood is not thoroughly dry. Free water and moisture must be driven off. If the hull has lain submerged, it may be necessary to let it air dry for a week or more under favorable atmospheric conditions before commencing repairs.

Larry Kean, a naval architect associated with Sparkman & Stephens, and Gene Rogers, completed this fine rebuilding job in their spare time, and went on to race the Highlander very successfully during the next summer season. The boat has since been sold, and Kean reports, from recent inspection, that the patches are in excellent condition and the boat appears serviceable for many years to come.

Spar Repair With Fiberglass

Fiberglass tape and an appropriate resin offer a fine system for repairing broken wooden spars. Restoration can be done easily and will add great permanent strength.

The fiberglass tape is woven from the same strong glass filaments used in the fiberglass cloth that is employed to cover wooden boats. Fiberglass tape is recommended for this type of job because of the ease of application and the desirability of laying up the glass yarn in a diagonal, spiral-wrap fashion.

Fiberglass tape is available in widths from 1½" up to about 12". Widths of 3" to 6" suffice for most jobs, but the narrower and wider dimensions are suggested for wrapping very small or very large spars.

Either epoxy or polyester resins can be used to bond the glass tape in place. While the epoxy type will offer greater adhesion, polyester is completely satisfactory because of the bandage-wrap system used.

Before proceeding with the repair, construction of the spar (hollow or solid) and the nature of the break must be considered. A tiller, oar or spar usually lets go with a long splintered break. Fortunately this type of fracture is easiest to repair because glass tape forces the splintered fragments back in their original position. If, however, the member breaks through at virtually 90°, wooden splints or a scarfed insert for a solid spar will have to be incorporated so that the tape will not be subjected to shear strain when a bending load is applied. A plug can be inserted in hollow spars and glued in place.

Estimating the need for splint-type temporary repair is mostly a case of judgment, but certainly would require the attention of a qualified expert if a big spar were involved. The simplified approach described herein will satisfy many situations which arise on small craft where the

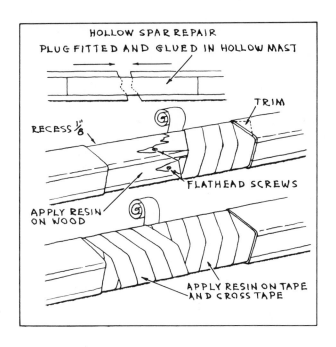

HOLLOW SPAR REPAIR
PLUG FITTED AND GLUED IN HOLLOW MAST

TRIM

RECESS 1/8"

FLATHEAD SCREWS

APPLY RESIN ON WOOD

APPLY RESIN ON TAPE AND CROSS TAPE

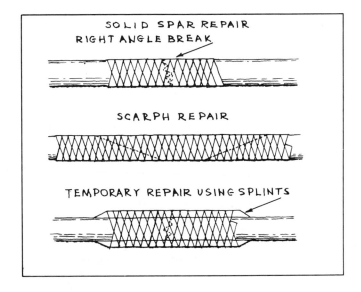

SOLID SPAR REPAIR
RIGHT ANGLE BREAK

SCARPH REPAIR

TEMPORARY REPAIR USING SPLINTS

owner normally expects to make his own repairs.

To explain the principles of a fiberglass-tape repair, let's consider a so-called compound fracture—a complete break— with long jagged ends. First of all, as indicated in the drawing accompanying, the broken parts should be coated with resorcinol (Elmer's waterproof) or epoxy glue and reassembled so that the alignment is true and the fit is as nearly perfect as possible. Screws can be used to bring splinters down flush and to make the glue line tight, or clamps can be used to accomplish the same purpose. After the glue is set, if you want a flush repair, cut a recess about 1/8'' deep, as shown, to allow space for the wrapping; then fill hollows with plastic wood.

The next step, spiral wrapping with the fiberglass tape, insures a dependable and lasting repair. The tape should be wound at about a 30° to 45° angle. In general, the glass wrapping should be carried several inches beyond the fractured portion onto the sound area of the wood. Butting the tape edges does a neater job. Except for a very light reinforcement, an additional layer should be applied in the opposite direction so a crisscross bandage of tape results. Tacks or staples are useful to hold the ends of the tape in place so that a tight fit can be achieved. A snug fit between wood and tape is important if the glass is to provide its full support when the repaired mast is stressed.

The resin may be applied in either of two ways. It may be brushed on preparatory to wrapping or you may impregnate the tape after it is dry-wrapped. However, each layer of tape should be saturated before the next one is applied. Thorough saturation of the glass fabric is important; and several tight layers of material do not always saturate thoroughly. This is particularly true with epoxy resin which tends to be quite viscous and will not easily permeate a dense build-up of fiberglass. After the repair has hardened to a tack-free consistency, sand the surface lightly and brush on a finish coat of resin so the cloth pattern is completely filled. The repair is now complete except for painting or varnishing.

Fixing A Leaking Centerboard Trunk With Fiberglass

Wooden centerboard trunks often develop chronic leaks that are difficult to eliminate by conventional means. Although many people understand the procedure of fiberglassing a hull or deck, there are a lot of questions on how to apply fiberglass to the centerboard area.

In most instances the leaks occur at the greatest point of strain in the structure, which is between the bottom of the box and the garboard. The principle of this repair is to apply the material at the point of entry of the water on the inside of the box, going as far up in the narrow slot as is practical. It is possible to run the material well above the static waterline in the box, but rarely possible to go much higher than this level. Since the water will tend to rise in the box when the boat is in motion, leakage may occur in the upper seams of a planked trunk. It is easiest to correct these leaks by sealing them with a regular compound, working from the inside of the boat where the affected area is completely accessible.

The system described here has been employed successfully many times on small centerboard craft. While the major fastenings of the box must be sound and tight, the fiberglass technique will help strengthen the joints as well as seal out water. It should obviate any necessity of completely demounting the box and re-seating it.

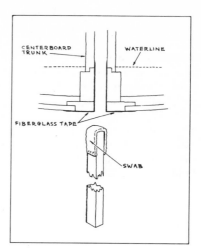

Detail of repair to leaky centerboard trunk, utilizing fiberglass tape as lining to waterproof the slot in the manner shown here. See text for further description of method.

Preparation

Remove the centerboard and turn the boat upside down, or roll her over on her side. The work will all be done from the outside.

The surface must be dry and free of paint or other residue. If the boat has just been hauled, drying of the wood can be accelerated by immediate cleaning and removing the paint.

Work from the outside, using a wood rasp to reach up into the box, and clean away the paint and accumulated marine growth. The object is to clean the wood as far up as possible, but practically speaking, you can't go much beyond six or eight inches.

Using the rasp and sandpaper, round off the corners to one-eighth or one-quarter inch radius. Rounding the sharp corners of the box will make the fiberglass fabric conform neatly. Carry the sanding operation over the garboard strake and the first plank. The joint between the garboard strake and the first plank is often a point of strain and resultant leakage and should be sealed thoroughly.

The next step is to provide a special tool to apply the resin into the narrow trunk slot. A stiff paint brush will allow you to get in an inch or so, but to reach in any distance, a thin, batten-shaped swab will be much more effective. Such an implement is undoubtedly well known to those who have applied bottom paint to the inside of the centerboard box. It can be made quickly by wrapping a flat stick with felt or cotton fabric or tacking burlap or old carpeting around the end of a lath.

Materials

Either epoxy or polyester resin can be used. A pint should be sufficient for most small sailboat trunks. Obtain some wide fiberglass tape (6″ or 12″) or fiberglass cloth, depending on availability and width requirements. Cut the fiberglass so that you have two strips which will run down each side of the trunk, leaving an inch at each end for overlap.

With the specially made swab, thoroughly coat the inside of the trunk with activated resin. Use a brush to saturate the area around the outside of the box. Then mold the pre-cut fiberglass panels down each side of the trunk carrying the fabric out over the garboard plank. Use the swab and your fingers in this operation. The excess fabric at the ends should be overlapped as neatly as possible using the swab and brush.

Essentially this is the complete technique. After the resin hardens, sand off the rough edges. If there appears to be an air bubble or some imperfection at any point, it is a simple matter to sand down the spot and add a small fiberglass patch.

CHAPTER 17

Covering With Fiberglass

THE PRACTICE OF COVERING WOODEN hulls and decks with fiberglass resin has been widely employed since World War II. Many an old wooden craft has been given a new lease on life with a fiberglassing job, and quite a few wood boats are being covered when built.

If properly applied, the covering will provide a seamless, leakproof sheathing for the deck or hull. The plastic surface will be easier to maintain and require less frequent painting to keep its appearance presentable. Particularly on small, light boats a single layer of fabric may considerably strengthen the structure and make it more resistant to impact damage. The fiberglass sheathing is also an effective barrier against marine parasites, particularly teredos and is often used where there is a special need to protect the underwater areas from worm attack.

Generally speaking, a fiberglass covering is most efficiently and economically employed when it is used only to protect the hull or deck surface and render them leakproof. For this reason it is recommended that the hull be structurally sound before proceeding with the fiberglass covering. Fiberglass cloth has a very high tensile strength, but any sizable boat needs a relatively thick skin of reinforced plastic to compensate for its structural weaknesses. The cost of the thicker fiberglass covering is usually very high compared to the cost of replacing or repairing frames and refastening, and then applying a thin, protective fiberglass sheathing.

Material Selection—Epoxy vs. Polyester Resin

Most boat covering is done today with polyester. Epoxy resins are, as discussed, known for their excellent adhesive characteristics; however, experience has shown that for most covering work polyester is perfectly adequate. Polyester is less expensive and easier to handle. Epoxy is employed only where there are special adhesion problems; i.e., covering metals, hardwoods such as oak, woods with high natural oil content, etc.

Fiberglass Fabrics

It is important that fiberglass fabric with the proper plastics compatibility be used. There have been some cases of unsuitable glass cloth being sold for covering that came on the market through surplus channels.

The design of the proper fabric is well standardized and widely available. Two weights are generally offered—a light weight about seven ounces per square yard and a nine-and-one-half ounce grade. The heavier weight cloth costs a bit more and takes a little more resin.

In our opinion, the heavier grade is best used on all boats except where the structure is small and light and where weight must be kept to a minimum.

The number of layers of fiberglass cloth to be applied depends on these factors—the boat's size, speed and power, the type of construction and structural condition.

Fiberglass tapes are offered in widths from about one inch to ten inches. Four and six inches are commonly available. Tapes are generally used in repair work (wrapping a broken tiller or spar) or, for example, sealing seams on a plywood hull.

Seam Fillers

Non-oil-base putties such as Duratite have generally been specified to fill seams, cracks, and gouges preparatory to fiberglassing. The reason is that oily compounds may inhibit a good resin bond. Chopped fiberglass and resin have also been used successfully, but such compounds cost more and are more trouble to apply. Polyester putties work well for filling gouges and cracks, but for extensive seam filling the material is probably not worth the cost. When applying fiberglass, the function of the seam filler is merely to fill and level any gaps in the surface so that the resin will not drain through.

Color Pigmentation Or Painting

Color can be added to the final coats of resin, or the unpigmented covering can be painted. It is an optional matter, but there are some factors to appreciate. The advantage of pigmented resin is the integral character of the colored finish. This is perhaps most important on a deck surface which will get considerable wear. However, on topsides it may prove best to use a conventional alkyd or epoxy paint system. It is difficult for instance to get the polyester color coat to flow on as evenly and smoothly as paint. Furthermore, light color pigments, such as white, do not hide the cloth pattern with great uniformity.

Application Questions—Expansion and Contraction

Fiberglass has a very small coefficient of elongation. Wood expands and contracts with moisture content, some types to a considerable degree.

From tests and field experience, several basic recommendations have resulted. For plywood structures which have little come and go, only one layer of glass cloth is necessary, except perhaps a doubling up at working joints. For planked hulls it is a matter of the width and thickness of the plank. Narrow planks, say about an inch wide, exert small lateral expansion and one layer of standard cloth appears to be quite adequate.

However, as the width approaches three and four inches, and considering the normal thickness of such planks, the expansion forces are considerable and two to three layers of cloth are necessary to restrain movement.

Weight Factor

A ten-ounce fabric laminated to the hull will weigh approximately four ounces per square foot. It is probably accurate to say that this weight only becomes a penalty in rare cases. On a 16' runabout, for instance, this would mean an added weight of about 20 pounds. However, it must be remembered that the weight is usually offset by the accumulated weight from water absorption in unprotected planking. Planked hulls can take on up to 30 percent of their weight in water absorption.

Heavily planked inboard skiff has been fiberglassed to a point above the waterline, stopping at the plank overlap. Two layers of fabric are necessary on such construction.

Covering Weakened Hull Structures

Where possible, weakened fastenings and important broken structural members should be replaced. Once this work has been accomplished, the remaining part can probably be reinforced with fiberglass. For one thing the fiberglass sheathing will hold the structure in place—prevent working and increase its integrity. This is particularly true with planked hulls. If many frames are cracked, and installing sister frames offers a monumental job, fiberglassing the cracked frames with several layers of cloth can be effective. Restoring small wooden boats (16' and under) in this fashion has worked well in our experience. In the case of larger craft, the amount of glass needed to do the job adequately appears to be out of proportion to what can properly be done with conventional wooden repair techniques.

Fiberglass cloth is laminated to planked deck using squeegee and brush. Rough edges will be trimmed and sanded after resin cures.

Wood Preparation

Preparation of the wood is important. To get a good long-lasting fiberglass covering the surface to which it is applied must be clean, dry, and as free as practicable from old paint. Stripping with a coarse disk sander is the recommended system, but certain non-wax paint removers can be used. Even if the wood is unpainted, sanding is necessary so that the pores of wood will be opened. The covering adheres by mechanical adhesion of the resin to the wood fibers; therefore, the surface glaze must be broken by sanding.

Cracks and seams must be filled with a non-oil-base putty, or a putty compounded from the resin and glass itself. Planks soaked with engine oil or woods with a natural high oil content, such as teak, must be neutralized. Washing down with a caustic solution (one pound of lye in a bucket of water) will be found effective for most conditions. Some workmen use carbon tetrachloride to remove oil desposits.

Except in the case of new unpainted hulls or decks, surface preparation is by far the biggest part of the overall job, but thoroughness is important.

It is desirable to have an unobstructed surface on which to lay the glass fabric. Therefore remove all hardware, coamings, bang plates, quarter rails, etc., that will come free.

Consideration Of Hulls

In order properly to direct boat owners on correct usage of fiberglass covering, it is helpful to analyze each type of wood-hull construction and objectively discuss what advantages have been experienced. To begin with, it must be remembered that fiberglassing has generally been more useful on older wooden boats where a protective coating is used to correct structural weakness or chronic leaking. This is not to say that newly constructed craft are not candidates, but that most builders prefer not to

Large mahogany planked power cruiser receiving fiberglass sheathing for worm protection.

Glass Plastics Co.

add the cost of a covering job to a stock hull. The one exception, however, concerns plywood hulls. Because of the special surface problems on plywood and the relative ease of covering this form of hull, it is quite common to find a fiberglass sheathing as a standard feature on new plywood boats.

Plywood Hulls

Small and large plywood hulls stand to gain quite a bit from a fiberglass covering. Plywood is also the easiest type of construction to handle. Regular marine fir plywood has a rather wild grain which is difficult to hide and is subject to checking. The covering will seal this condition and minimize surface upkeep. Because expansion and contraction are small, due to small number of seams, a single layer of cloth can be used on the continuous panels. At the joints, such as chine, stem or transom, the fiberglass should be doubled up. The job can be simplified by applying 4" or 6" fiberglass tape to the various joints and connections before proceeding with the application of the wide fabric. The only exception to this reinforcing procedure is in the case of small plywood prams or light skiffs.

Smooth Plank (Carvel) Construction

Consideration of carvel construction breaks down into two classifications—narrow planking and wide. The modern "Down East" strip-building technique of edge-nailed, glued construction is extremely strong and watertight. However, many older hulls have a tendency to loosen up and leak. A single layer of ten-ounce fiberglass cloth laminated over this type has provided an effective watertight envelope. Extra layers of reinforcement must be used at working joints, such as stern, garboard and transom.

Wide-planked carvel hulls are rarely covered at the time they are built unless the owner wishes a sheathing for worm protection or perhaps for running in ice. However, many such older hulls which have loosened up may be effectively sealed by the application. Because the wide, heavy planks exert considerable expansion and contraction forces, two or three layers of ten-ounce glass fabric are necessary to resist movement and prevent splitting the covering. The need for extra laminations on this type of construction is irrespective of the size and weight of hull. Wide planks (say three-inches and above) do exhibit considerable expansion forces that have to be restrained.

Lapstrake Construction

Lapstrake hulls are very popular today. By using modern adhesives and seam sealers, this form of wood construction has been vastly improved. But, as they get old, lapstrake hulls begin to work and loosen up, causing annoying leakage. Some such boats become logical candidates for a fiberglass application. The special techniques and consideration used on this type of irregular surface provide guidance for other complicated deck or hull areas.

Fiberglassing this type of hull is not an easy job. It should not be attempted without some prior experience with the materials, and it requires a planned procedure. Small clinker hulls, because they can be worked on in an inverted position, simply require patience and "molding" skill. Larger craft that cannot be turned over must be progressively laminated with relatively narrow panels of glass cloth. Because of the working position and the size of the area to be done, several workmen are usually necessary to do the job.

Preparation

Following normal fiberglassing practice, the planking must be stripped of paint and be clean and dry. The edges of the strakes should be rounded off to about a 3/16″ radius to facilitate molding of the cloth. Regarding treatment of the seam joints, some people prefer to tack on quarter-round strips so that the cloth will form easily and tightly. However, this method decidedly affects the appearance of a finely straked hull and is not considered necessary from a functional standpoint. The resin-saturated cloth can be worked down far enough against the joint without the assist of a filler strip. Some bridging will exist, but by "doctoring" the cloth with resin, a complete seal can be made.

Resin

Regardless of which resin is chosen (polyester or epoxy), its particular consistency is important when laminating to a lapstrake hull. Unless the brushed-on resin has a degree of tackiness, it will be excessively difficult to make the cloth stay in place. Fiberglass does not stretch (although there may be some nominal yield due to the nature of the weave). Furthermore, glass fibers spring back and will not hold to a sharp radius unless held in some manner. Consequently, it is worthwhile to obtain a covering resin which has been formulated to work well on irregular contours.

If it is desirable to have a very high degree of tackiness (perhaps the

Rolling fiberglass cloth into resin primed surface of lapstrake dinghy.

Photos by Glass Plastics Co.

Using a pair of rubber squeegees to form cloth around strakes.

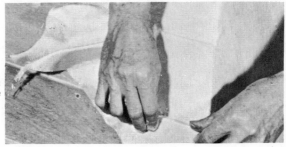

Forming cloth from transom around sides of lapstrake sided skiff.

job calls for laminating an overhead surface where the cloth tends to pull away), consider two possibilities. Allow the brushed-on resin to set for a while and increase in tackiness. Or, consider using a highly filled epoxy compound. Such epoxy products have great viscosity and the glass cloth will bed and hold very nicely.

Holding Devices

When covering resins and techniques were less perfected great reliance was placed on mechanical means of holding the cloth in place. Tacks, staples, battens, and other similar devices were used. But because glass does not stretch like canvas, such fasteners are only partially effective. A neater and faster job can be done by molding the fabric in place and only using mechanical holding devices where they are clearly the answer.

Cloth Technique

The standard weight boat cloth (about 9.5 to 10 oz. per sq. ft.) adapts well to covering lapstrake hulls. The material has good body and forming characteristics. Lighter weight fabrics can, of course, be used, but cloth lighter than about six ounces seems to "float" a bit in the resin film and is tricky to handle.

One layer of fabric is usually adequate for hulls under 18', although an extra ply will be needed if the boat is working badly or subject to excessive abuse, high speed, etc. Local reinforcing laminations can be easily applied. For hulls above 20', two-ply is minimum. In addition, the

Fiberglassing large catamaran of plywood construction at Stonington Boat Works (right). Chine seams are reinforced with tape. Note butting of fabric panels and usage of white epoxy compound overhead to better hold fabric (below).

Louis S. Martel

Using paint roller to apply white pigmented resin on fiberglass cloth.

Glass Plastics Co.

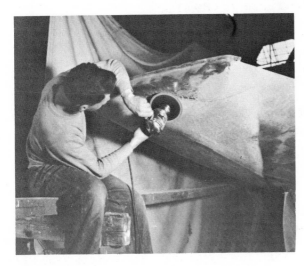

Victory Class sloop receiving fiberglass hull covering. Boat's racing performance was markedly improved by the watertight sheathing.

Owens-Corning

structure should be sound in its own right, for a thin layer or two of fiberglass cannot hold together a large wooden hull that is in a weakened condition.

Fiberglass boat cloth is available in a variety of widths—commonly, 38", 44" and 60". The 44-inch width will handle well for most jobs. Preliminary planning on how the cloth is to be laid on the hull will save time and effort once the project is underway. We have observed that some people are over-cautious about working with wide widths and have applied the material in tape form or narrow panels. This is not necessary and will make for more work in the end because of the sanding operation necessary to provide a smooth surface at the edges.

Small hulls are naturally covered in an inverted position. In this case the fabric should be applied fore and aft. The cloth is rolled out in wet resin. Form the fabric in the strakes by beginning at the middle and progress forward and aft on each strake. It is usually best to start down at the sheer and progress upwards, pulling the loose gather of cloth down into the seams. A rubber squeegee, or perhaps two—one in each hand—are useful tools, but inevitably you will want to use your fingers to do the final touches.

In the case of large hulls which cannot be turned over, running the cloth panels athwartship may be much more practical. Such boats will require two layers of fabric and therefore panels can be butted and staggered between plies. The covering of large lapstrake hulls is greatly facilitated by heeling them over as far as is practicable. The previously mentioned resin techniques and holding devices may be necessary in certain areas.

COVERING SPECIAL TYPES OF CRAFT:

Canoes

The question repeatedly comes up whether one can cover over the existing canvas surface. This is possible, but not advisable. The objective is to get the new fiberglass skin to bond intimately with the planking. Too, light weight is desirable with a canoe. It is best to strip the paint-loaded canvas and build up a fresh cover of glass.

Kayaks

We have not had personal experience in fiberglassing kayaks. The following comments reflect opinions from those who have covered this type of craft.

There are two methods which have been used to fiberglass kayaks—applying glass cloth over the canvas and applying glass over the bare framework. In the former method, the surface must be roughened with sandpaper so that the glass lamination will establish a mechanical bond. In the latter method, it is suggested that a fine weave cloth be used so that the liquid resin has less of a tendency to drain through. Initial applications of resin must be carefully applied until all the pores in the fabric are sealed.

Steel And Aluminum Boats

Very little fiberglassing of metal boats has been done. Since the major justification is for preventing corrosion, there are any number of alternate protective coatings which can be applied with less cost and labor.

In the case of aluminum, fiberglassing has generally been confined to taping seams and repair of punctures. Aluminum is a difficult material with which to get a good bond. When using fiberglass, epoxy resin must be used. The metal must be carefully cleaned and scoured with an abrasive.

Steel is easier to bond to than aluminum, but here again epoxy resin is recommended. The surface must be clean and free of rust and scale. If the steel surface has a zinc protective coating, you will not get a bond; the zinc or galvanized finish will have to be removed with a sandblast.

As a general principle in fiberglassing, use epoxy resins for laminating to any extensive area of metal surface. This recommendation would apply to all metals associated with boats—iron, steel, lead, copper, bronze, aluminum, etc. Polyesters can be used successfully on steel, but generally they are specially formulated compounds. An example is seen in the automotive body putties. While these polyester putties lend themselves to small area repairs, they are impractical for extensive covering with fiberglass cloth.

Fiberglassing Metal Centerboards

The surface on a corroded and pitted iron centerboard can be completely restored with the use of fiberglass cloth and epoxy resin. Epoxy is, of course, used here because of its superior adhesion to metals.

All the loose scale and rust must be knocked off with a hammer and cold chisel. The metal need not be worked to a burnished condition, but the surface should be sound and free of any dust or contamination. Lay the board in a horizontal position and apply the glass cloth and resin to one side at a time—allowing the resin to harden before turning it over. Carry the cloth around the edges, double up the fabric at the bottom of the board where it is likely to encounter impact and abrasion. Make an effort to do a smooth job as a rough board will contribute drag when moving through the water.

Boat owners are also reporting considerable success in simply brushing on epoxy resin on metal boards without using the fiberglass fabric. This is a simpler technique, but naturally it is not so durable a coating.

Fiberglassing Wooden Centerboards

Assuming that the slot is wide enough to accept the centerboard thickened by resin and fiberglass, proceed in the same manner as with a metal board. Make sure the board is dry, clean and rough-sanded before fiberglassing.

CHAPTER 18

Fiberglass Boat Evaluation

ALTHOUGH FIBERGLASS CONSTRUCTION shows an increasing acceptance every year, and despite the successful performance of the vast majority of these boats, there are still questions raised about their characteristics and the material with which they are constructed. The most searching questions usually come from the experienced and thoughtful yachtsman who has, through many years of familiarity with wood and metal craft, developed a fine sense of appreciation for performance, quality, and detail. The following discussion is not by any means all-inclusive, but it is hoped that it represents the most common questions which come up.

Are Fiberglass Boats Susceptible To Heat Or Cold?

Normally the thought behind this question is whether the material becomes rigid or brittle in freezing temperatures and soft or pliable under heat. An incorrect association is made between thermoplastic products, like plastic garden hose or a plastic raincoat, which exhibit limp to rigid characteristics under hot and cold conditions. The thermosetting polyester resin used to laminate fiberglass boats is simply not affected by the normal range of atmospheric temperature to which a boat is exposed. As far as cold goes, a fiberglass-polyester laminate actually exhibits a small increase in strength as the temperature is dropped to some 60° below zero. In the opposite direction, physical strengths show no measurable fall-off until temperatures reach close to 200° F. The fibrous glass, in any event, has a far greater resistance to heat and actually upgrades the heat-resistant factor of the plastic itself by acting as a stable, heat-dissipating element of the combination.

Some proof of performance is offered by various products which operate in climatic extremes. Fiberglass snow sleds have been used successfully in the Arctic by the military, as well as snow skis for aircraft and sports. The Dew Line radar installations which protect our northern continental boundaries are housed in fiberglass-reinforced plastic domes. At the other end of the temperature range, fiberglass-reinforced plastic is being used in the nose cones of missiles where searing heat is encountered. While higher heat-distortion resins than polyester are used in this application, the example shows what can be done with proper

Cross section of Mobjack sailboat hull, showing use of low and high density foam plastics for high panel stiffness and integral flotation.

engineering. It goes without saying that the polyester-glass laminate in a boat hull will retain its full strength under any torrid atmospheric conditions which it may encounter.

Weight Characteristics Of Fiberglass Construction

We have heard a great many opinions on this subject. Some people feel that fiberglass boats are too heavy; an almost equal number say they are too light. For an analysis, the question actually has to be broken down into categories of craft and considered in the light of design.

As a basic fact, there is nothing inherent in this construction material which requires that a boat be either light or heavy; it is a matter of how it is engineered and put together. Fiberglass-plastic has an extremely high strength-to-weight ratio, which means the designer is free to impart the weight and distribution of weight he wishes. Some engineering factors affecting weight are perhaps pertinent. Planked wooden boats are usually heavily constructed in order to maintain stiffness of structure to prevent working and leaking. A seamless fiberglass hull does not need such allowances. Aluminum construction is a still different matter; compensation must be made for the relative weakness of joints, the overall ductility of the material, and the corrosion factor.

As a justifiable criticism of fiberglass boats, many early outboards and dinghies were excessively heavy because a thick hull shell was built up to give rigidity, rather than using a more efficient lightweight framing or sandwich technique. In short, the problem has been a matter of design and construction technique rather than any basic drawback of the material itself.

Noise And Vibration Characteristics

Fiberglass-plastic, being a hard, dense composition, does transmit sound and vibration to a somewhat greater degree than wood, but its dampening characteristics are far closer to wood than metal. The relatively thin, flexible monocoque shell which is generally employed in fiberglass construction probably has more to do with the resultant effect than any inherent property of the material. There is, compared to a wood hull, less volume of material to absorb the energy generated.

Negative comments regarding this characteristic seem neither general nor profuse. A lot depends on how the boat is constructed. For instance, new foam and sandwich construction seen in hulls of small boats and decks of larger ones impart excellent noise-reduction qualities.

Flotation Qualities

If a fiberglass boat is swamped, it will not float of its own accord unless buoyancy chambers are provided. The specific density of the material is at least twice that of wood. Reserve buoyancy is, therefore, provided in small craft like outboards and day sailers either by air tanks or by chunks of foamed plastic. The foam type is perhaps the more reliable, but air chambers or tanks have been approved by the Coast Guard for years. However, it is important for the prospective owner to check the amount of reserve buoyancy furnished. It is desirable to have enough to support the engine and other fixed equipment, as well as providing a make-shift life raft for partly submerged passengers.

It must be further understood that not all types of boats can, for practical considerations, be kept afloat adequately after capsizing. For instance, a high-speed 12′ runabout with a heavy outboard engine might require so much space for flotation that there would be little or no room for the passengers. In large cruisers with heavy ballast or engines, the same practical problems must be considered. In such craft, hatch arrangements, bulkheads, compartments and seaworthiness of hull are the defenses against sinking.

The important point is that the owner must understand the reserve buoyancy and seaworthiness characteristics of his boat so that he can estimate his risks under varying conditions.

Lightning Protection

Investigations made regarding lightning and fiberglass boats reveal that damage from electric discharge seems to be rare, but does appear to be of practical concern for the sailboat owner.

Most modern cruising auxiliaries have the upper shrouds and metal spars bonded to a common ground such as the keel. Small sailboats rarely seem to have a grounding system incorporated. At any rate, fiberglass hulls need to be properly grounded just as wooden hulls. A glass laminate is, in fact, a better insulator than a wooden one.

One might ask what happens to a glass hull if it is struck by a lightning bolt. A case we observed is perhaps worth relating. The particular fiberglass boat was a 16' day sailer with an aluminum spar. The lightning hit the mast, was conducted down to the mast step where it jumped a short distance and punched a three-inch hole through the bottom of the hull. Whether this is the typical or expected result of a strike is hard to say. The voltage potential in a bolt is enormously high, and the path that it may travel is never certain unless a grounding system provides an easy route of escape. We have heard, for instance, of unprotected wooden hulls which have had virtually all of their fastenings started by an unusually severe strike.

Safety

Good design and construction in fiberglass offers the maximum in safety; this is naturally an important factor for the boat owner. The resilient, high-impact properties of the material, as well as the seamless continuity of the structure make such performance possible. We are continually receiving dramatic and interesting verification on the strength of these hulls. Some years ago, for instance, one of the 40' Bountys fell off the ways at an eastern yard. Being a deep-keeled hull she hit with tremendous force on her side. The damage to the hull was very minor and localized at the point of impact. Another case is that of a 40' Block Island yawl which was involved in a bizarre accident. Moored in a quiet Long Island harbor one night, with a full crew sleeping aboard, she was rammed amidships by a pilotless tugboat. The force of impact was so great that it made a shambles of the interior of the yawl and snapped the adjacent steel shrouds. But the hull shell itself only sustained a small, localized crack where the tug's bow hit. Considering the disrupted interior, it was clear that the fiberglass hull had deflected inwards a great distance, but returned to its original fair shape with no permanent distortion.

Impact and Hurricanes

The impact energy absorbing qualities so unique to fiberglass-plastic laminates are very dramatically shown in the Coast Guard drop tests performed on fiberglass lifeboats. Fully loaded, they have been dropped from ten feet into water with little or no damage. While such a severe test has never been tried on wood or metal lifeboats, it is questionable whether critical points like the seams could remain serviceably tight.

Hurricanes take a big toll of pleasure craft. Checks with insurance companies following storms indicate that fiberglass construction is a good risk. Several yacht brokers who follow their clients' activities and problems rather closely feel that fiberglass boats come through big storms very well.

Maintenance Costs

The biggest appeal, of course, in fiberglass construction is greatly reduced maintenance. While this feature is thoroughly appreciated by the small boat owner, low maintenance costs are many times more important to the big boat operator. Surveys show that a large number of yacht owners are obliged by economic necessity to do the major portion of their routine maintenance. The amount of time and money expended on this ritual also appears to be a major factor in an individual determining whether he wants to buy a sizable cruising boat. To the extent that fiberglass construction can greatly reduce this burden, we can expect that the material will promote wider big-boat ownership.

All the advantages of fiberglass construction take on magnified meaning and importance in bigger craft. For instance, an individual might put up with an afternoon of wetness in a leaking, planked outboard or sailboat, but transfer this condition to a cruising boat out for several days and it can be acutely uncomfortable.

Freedom from worry about deterioration is a major factor for the boat owner. Fiberglass-plastic cannot be attacked by worms and will not be involved in electrolytic problems, for it is an insulator. Freedom from rot, corrosion, etc., are, of course, well understood advantages. The necessity for haul-out inspections is greatly reduced. The owner can afford to leave his craft in the water or in dry storage without worrying about the many elements which threaten wood and metal construction.

How Long Will A Fiberglass Boat Last?

A most common question about fiberglass boats concerns their long-term durability. How long are they supposed to last? Has an average life been established? What effects can be noticed after years of hard usage?

As a matter of record, yachts constructed of conventional materials, well built and properly maintained, stay in active service for many years—20, 30, and over 50 years is not uncommon with wooden construction. This kind of potential durability in older construction becomes a measure of longevity for a new material such as fiberglass.

It has been demonstrated that fiberglass requires less maintenance. But there lurks the question in many minds as to the long-term performance of fiberglass. Does it maintain its strength? Will the resin "crystallize" or break down? Are there undiscussed physical changes of a deteriorating nature which take place?

These fears have not been realized. There are many physical examples demonstrating excellent long-term durability. For instance, one of the first Chevrolet Corvette automobiles (built in 1953) was recently given a thorough inspection. Except for repairs from several collisions the body structure looked practically the same as the day it was molded. The car had been driven more than 150,000 miles. The performance demonstrated by laboratory samples and finished articles, such as the car body, are convincing indicators. But the boatman really wants this translated directly into marine terminology.

Some time ago Owens-Corning instituted a search to locate early large fiberglass boats for study. The Navy had molded the earliest large fiberglass craft back in 1946 and 1947. They were 26' personnel boats fabricated by Winner Manufacturing Co. Some of these craft are still being used, but were not readily available for inspection. What we did find were three 40' Coast Guard patrol boats which were then ten years old. The Coast Guard was interested in a cooperative study and evaluation that could provide additional knowledge for their expanding usage of fiberglass boats. Routine service reports indicated that the 40-footers had stood up well during the ten years and that maintenance costs incurred were one-fifth the costs of steel craft of the same age and service duration. However, a thorough study of the hulls had never been made. It was decided to make a careful inspection and, furthermore, to cut square-foot panels out of the hulls for laboratory analysis.

These 40' patrol craft are a familiar design and are known to all who cruise our coastal and Great Lakes waters. They have a long, lean profile and low, uncluttered superstructure, and are 40'3" l.o.a., 11'3" beam, and are of 21,000 displacement. They are driven at a top speed of 22 knots by twin 250-h.p. diesels. The structural design of the fiberglass 40-footers was developed on a cooperative basis between the Coast Guard and The Anchorage, Inc., of Warren, R.I., pioneers in fiberglass construction. The

Owens-Corning

Ten year old 40-foot fiberglass Coast Guard patrol craft hauled for repairs and survey. Hull is in sound, fair condition. Note absence of bottom paints. Anti-fouling protection not necessary in chemically polluted waters of Houston Ship Channel.

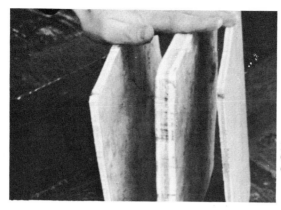

result was a rugged, single-skin shell of fiberglass for cabin and hull, and a bottom web frame of aluminum "I" sections. The aluminum sections were to perform a stiffening function and load-distributing structure for the heavy and powerful diesel engines. The use of wood was confined to such elements as the sheer clamp, cockpit sole and shelf. The fiberglass laminate was composed of a combination of ten-ounce cloth and mat, the bottom about 3/4", topsides and deck 3/8".

The service records of the craft indicated hard and continuous use. Operating hours and age were as follows: CG-40502, delivered April, 1952—7600 hours; CG-40503, delivered October, 1952—6800 hours; CG-40504, delivered February, 1953—4300 hours. Service was in both salt and fresh water. In 1962 all three were operating in the Houston Ship Canal.

They were selected for this duty because of the highly corrosive waters of the Canal, which are extremely hard on the steel boats. Apparently, waste dumped into the canal from the oil and gas refineries resulted in a destructive concentration of sulphuric acid. The fiberglass hulls showed no effect from this exposure even though one boat had served there since 1954.

We journeyed to Houston with officials from the Coast Guard to make a thorough study of these fiberglass patrol crafts. The oldest boat had been hauled at Seabrook for engine replacement and various other repairs. The fiberglass-covered plywood cockpit sole and other similar sections had been removed for ease of inspection. The other two boats were on station in the Houston Canal.

In the course of observation and discussion we learned that some design modifications had been necessary to correct certain troublesome areas in all three boats. Transom sections had been modified and the midship portion of the wooden sheer clamp had sustained stress cracks from hitting pilings and large heavy craft. But the impressive and significant fact was that the basic fiberglass hull and deck laminates were in excellent condition. The boats had been periodically painted to maintain their fresh appearance, but there was no denting, distortion, or decomposition of the material.

The soundness of the fiberglass laminate was strikingly evident when square-foot panels were cut from several areas of the CG-40502. Portions were sawed out of the cabin top, topsides, and bottom. Evidence of the good condition of the laminate can be seen in the accompanying photograph. While the bilges of the boat were coated with an unavoidable accumulation of oil and dirt and the bottom stained from growth and foul water, the freshly cut edges of the sawed-out panels showed no penetration of these contaminates. Without exception, the inside of the laminate looked as good as the day it was laid up.

The panels were sent to a materials laboratory for physical tests. The specific strengths of the laminate at the time of molding are not known. But the strength values after this ten-year period were more than adequate for the vessels' design requirements. The values, while lower than usually attained today, with improved glass and resin materials, appear to be consistent with data on file from the early 1950's.

The reader may be curious about the aluminum web frame in these boats. This was a special design feature requested by the Coast Guard at the time the craft were conceived. It is our belief that the selection of the aluminum frames at that period of fiberglass development had to do with two requirements—adequate stiffening and, perhaps more important, a durable frame system which would facilitate the mounting of engines.

The aluminum "I" channels had suffered to some extent from corrosion, though not seriously. A bituminous coating had been partially effective in sealing the surface of the metal. The base flange of the "I" pieces had been fiberglassed over to lock them into the laminate. This bond had broken down in places, but it did not seem to have caused any operating troubles.

It is worthwhile to point out that incorporation of metal in this manner is quite uncommon in today's fiberglass boats, because of the problems of bonding, corrosion, and general structural incompatibility. Fiberglass boats of this size constructed in the past few years generally use heavy, hollow fiberglass longitudinals which are incorporated into the laminate shell.

The Coast Guard Port Commander at Houston was pleased with the service of the boats and the manner in which they had stood up to hard duty. He cited two incidents which were noteworthy.

One patrol boat had her rudder linkage break when cruising down the channel. Out of control and at substantial speed she veered into the side of a big steel barge. The bow was crushed back several feet, but there was no other damage. Some local fiberglass mechanics repaired the bow section in several days. We looked over the repaired boat and were impressed by the good job and the fact that the break between the old and new material was not discernible.

Another operational case pointed out an advantage of the fiberglass hull. The Port of Houston has had some serious tanker fires. During one conflagration a fiberglass boat and a steel patrol boat were dispatched to the accident scene. The crew of the fiberglass boat were able to operate closer to the intense heat from the flames and for a longer period of time than that of the steel hull because of the low heat-conductive nature of the fiberglass boat. It was, furthermore, pointed out that while the topsides paint was scorched, the laminate did not ignite nor was it otherwise damaged. These boats were not molded with fire-retardent resin, since such resin was not available in the early 1950's.

The survey of these Coast Guard boats was certainly a constructive study for both the participating parties. The sound condition of the fiberglass-polyester laminates confirms the fact that the material will stand up to hard usage in a marine environment.

The modifications which were made were a result of unsatisfactory design details. At the time of building not much was known about proper structural reinforcement of large, heavy glass powerboats. The models were in most respects copies from the steel type.

But even with modification costs included in the maintenance figure, the total cost was 80 percent less than the upkeep on the steel models.

A 20-Year Survey

The foregoing survey of the 40-foot fiberglass patrol boats was conducted in 1961. In 1971 one of these three vessels was finally retired from service in Miami, Florida. Test panels were again cut from the bottom. No physical degradation was evident. The cut edges had the same fresh appearance as the specimens examined ten years previously. Physical strength properties showed no depreciation. The hull had served almost twenty years of constant and rigorous service.

Comparisons Between Fiberglass and Wood Scantlings

It is not unusual for technically inclined individuals who are evaluating fiberglass as a boat-building material to try to establish some sort of equivalence between wood and the newer material. A typical question which comes up concerns a comparison of strength for a given thickness; i.e., "How thick does a fiberglass hull have to be if the wooden counterpart is of a given dimension?"

Most qualified fiberglass engineers will refuse to answer such a question unless many points of construction and performance are known. This attitude on the part of the knowledgeable specialist, rather than being evasive, is actually honest and accurate. Tables of equivalency between the two materials are very difficult to establish with accuracy because of their dissimilarities. Precise comparisons which can be made are of a limited and specific nature.

It is perhaps obvious, in comparing structural materials, that the most accurate evaluation is made by conducting the comparison within the context of a particular design. This point is important because most developments in fiberglassplastic are seamless units with relatively few joints and connections. A fiberglass boat hull exhibits certain strength characteristics which result from the nature of the design as much as from the specific properties of the material itself.

Functional Strength Sources

Modern fiberglass filaments are among the strongest materials known today. To be specific, pure filaments will deliver tensile strength up to 700,000 pounds per square inch (p.s.i.). High-performance, laminated aero-space components are realizing over 200,000 p.s.i. Less sophisticated structures like boat hulls are achieving up to 50,000 p.s.i. Such high-strength characteristics are important to successful performance, but it is only part of the story.

Fiberglass-plastic contributes unusually good impact properties. This is important in a boat hull. The material is extremely resilient, can absorb a great deal of energy and, because of high elasticity, returns to its original shape without distortion.

There are, then, two desirable material-strength properties which are, so to speak, inherent. There is also a third strength aspect. It is often ignored, but is, perhaps, most important when comparing fiberglass to traditional wood-boat construction. This is the strength integrity made possible by a monocoque, seamless design. A wooden boat is only as strong as her fastenings. The fastenings are susceptible to corrosion. Planking will work under stress and fastenings may loosen. Generally speaking, framing members, which add so much to the weight of a wooden hull, are there simply to hold the planks in position and to prevent the structure from working and leaking. A glass hull, on the other hand, has a seamless shell with very few frames and no built-in stresses.

In some designs, frames and longitudinals are necessary to distribute concentrated loads and to stiffen the shell, but the fundamental monocoque-shell design is much more efficient. This is one important reason why we find molded fiberglass boats weighing so much less than their planked-wood counterparts. Weight savings up to 30 percent have been observed.

Before leaving this discussion of comparison, it is essential to note that modern wood technology has achieved means of weight savings. Sheet plywood panels and, particularly, molded plywood yield a much more efficient strength-to-weight ratio than does conventional planked construction.

Flexibility—An Advantage and a Design Problem

Fiberglass-plastic has a low modulus of stiffness compared to wood and metals. This feature can be readily seen in thin, flat unsupported boat panels. Such panels, of course, are highly resilient. They will return to their original shape even after extreme deflection. This property is one important reason why impact resistance is high. It can also be the source of trouble in a poorly designed structure. A typical example would be a fiberglass bottom or topside which is too easily deflected, and the resultant strain is abruptly concentrated at a stiffening frame or bulkhead. In the trade such a condition is called a "hard spot." Repeated flexing of the unsupported panel can cause a laminate failure at this sharply rigid point.

Panel flexing is not in itself a feature to be condemned. It is a matter of how the resultant strains are transferred and relieved. A well designed, thin structure can take an extraordinary amount of abuse because the ability to yield means that the energy of impact is greatly absorbed. I recall one accident which showed this characteristic quite dramatically. A 16′ inboard-powered, fiberglass runabout was rammed amidship by another boat. The runabout had a thin, well-shaped side shell. A wooden sheer clamp was the major stiffening member. Under the impact of collision, the side of the runabout gave in almost to the engine box, but popped back again to its proper shape. The wood clamp broke, but only surface damage was sustained by the shell. If a rigid frame or transverse member had been adjacent to impact, undoubtedly the laminate would have sheared through.

In summary then, the resilient impact-absorbing properties of a fiberglass laminate can be effectively utilized in the design of a boat. Thin laminates can perform remarkably well if used with intelligence and discretion. Limberness in the structure, however, should never be tolerated beyond a functional point. That is to say, decks should be firm and secure under foot, bottom panels should be stiff enough to give a planing surface free of distortion at designed speeds and loading, and the topsides should be rigid enough to withstand rough docking maneuvers or similar operational conditions.

Load in Tons	U.S. Requirements 1½" x 2½" E. Oak on 1" Planking	Lloyds Rules 3½" x 2⅞" E. Oak on 1⅜" Planking	Halmatic Hollow Frame 3⅜" 1⅞" x 3" Hollow Frame ½" Laminate
		Deflection in Inches	
1.0	0.2	0,05	**0.11**
1.25	0.3		
1.5	0.45	0.15	0.225
1.75	Broken		
2.0		0.26	0.36
2.5		0.43	0.5
3.0		0.7	0.64
3.5		1.0	0.8
4.0		Broken	0.975
4.5			Broken but skin intact and watertight

Not to be overlooked, and very important, is the fact that shape can increase panel stiffness to a very large degree. This is, of course, true in wood or any other material, but it is of natural importance to fiberglass. The material needs stiffening, and it is easy to develop any type of curvature because no fabrication limitation is imposed.

A Scantling Comparison

Because of the differences in material properties between wood and fiberglass, it is difficult to establish accurate and meaningful equivalent data tables. There have been some specific studies made which are indicative. The following is an actual destructive test experiment conducted on the Halmatic (English firm) fiberglass construction system versus the wood scantling requirements as put forth by Lloyd's and U.S. requirements. The vessel used for the test was a 67', 32-ton yacht built by Halmatic to designs of John G. Alden. Comparative tests were conducted on 1' x 3' framed panels. Since the framing on the Halmatic panels is similar to the transverse framing used in wooden hulls the tests are of particular significance.

CHAPTER 19

Aspects Regarding Fire

FIRE ABOARD BOATS has been a deep concern from the earliest days, and is certainly no less so today. Modern engineering has done much to reduce the fire hazard, but it still exists and precautions must be observed.

Among the many points raised about fiberglass boats has been the flammability question. How does the material react when exposed to flame? Is there a greater danger from fire with fiberglass craft than with boats constructed of wood or metal? Fiberglass-plastic construction poses no more fire danger for pleasure craft than any other conventional material. And with certain design and construction features taken into consideration, there can be shown some important improvements. These aspects will be discussed below.

Evaluation of fire resistance is quite a complicated subject. No material is completely immune to the effects of an open flame and high heat. It is a matter of degree and how the particular substance reacts when exposed to a conflagration. While steel and concrete will not burn, buildings constructed of these materials may collapse if the interior fire reaches sufficient intensity. The fact that a material will not support combustion is not necessarily the prime criterion of safety. For example, steel beams can yield and buckle from high heat while wooden beams, in a severely charred condition, will often hold the integrity of a structure for a critically important period of time. The real question, then, is the matter of proper engineering and design, and whether the material in question fulfills the primary safety requirements for the particular end use.

Combustibility Of Polyester Resin

Fiberglass, of course, will not burn, but the polyester resin used in most molded boats will support a flame. The normal type of boat laminate can be ignited and will burn with about the same intensity as plywood. The flame-spread rating, too, is approximately the same as wood. Burning resin releases a black, sooty smoke.

Self-extinguishing polyester resins are used in military craft, lifeboats and by some builders of large pleasure boats. These resins will not support combustion when the source of flame is removed, have a lower flame-spread rating, and are a bit more difficult to ignite. While there have been efforts to push the fiberglass boat industry towards the general adoption of fire-retardant resins, it is our belief that, for a number of technical reasons, this is unnecessary.

Material Fire Safety Criteria

Wood has been the standard of comparison for many engineering aspects in the small boat industry., including fire. In large passenger vessels, where the fire peril is more acute and modern regulations are very strict, steel and other non-combustible materials are carefully specified.

Fire resistance of wood varies greatly as to type. More important than this, every boat is coated with paint. Unless the paint is of a flame-retardant variety, it may burn quite fiercely. As an added factor, oil-soaked planks may contribute to the conflagration.

If a boat is of steel construction, the fact that the metal will not burn may certainly provide some measure of safety, but as a general rule the combustible furnishings will create the major hazard and, in the process of burning, may render the stell hull quite useless after the fire is over. The reader may be aware that steel yachts do not enjoy any special reduction in insurance rates over wood. There are a number of special reasons for this fact, but at least we can see that the fire hazard has not been eliminated through steel construction.

Acceptance Of Fiberglass Lifeboats

Coast Guard approval of fiberglass lifeboats for all passenger and cargo vessels illustrates some interesting points on the fire question. Steel and aluminum lifeboats have been accepted for a good number of years. When fiberglass was first considered, the flammability question was debated. It was pointed out that under exposure to intense heat, steel lifeboats became too hot to touch, or their seam gaskets burned out. Aluminum lifeboats, in the intense heat of tanker fires, have been known to melt. It was reasoned that a fiberglass-plastic laminate had significantly lower heat-conduction factor and that a glass lifeboat would offer at least equal serviceability under such extreme fire conditions.

Some Practical Considerations

The same precautions against fire should be observed in operating a fiberglass boat as with boats constructed of any other material. There are definite Coast Guard requirements on the type and placement of fire extinguishers, and gasoline carburetors must have an approved-type flame arrestor.

When the special processing difficulties of self-extinguishing polyester resins have been worked out, they undoubtedly will be used more widely by boat builders. Nevertheless, there are any number of sensible safety features which can be incorporated into a cruising boat, power or sail, to give a high degree of protection. Fire resistant paints or coatings can be applied to the interior of the hull or perhaps in local areas such as the engine compartment. Glassfiber insulation can be used to line the engine box or compartment. Metal shielding in the galley stove area is probably a wise idea—as much to prevent defacement of the glass or wood ceiling as outright flame protection.

How Fiberglass Fuel Tanks Resist Fire

New England residents will recall the Essex Boat Yard fire which occurred January 20, 1968. There have been few boat yard disasters of this nature which have been as dramatically destructive; consequently, some of the effects of it have drawn considerable attention.

Those of us associated with the fiberglass industry were especially interested because so many fiberglass yachts were destroyed or damaged. But the one incident which received the most publicity was the condition of two fiberglass fuel tanks. They emerged from the center of the holocaust remarkably intact and, most surprising of all, still containing some gasoline.

Very often disasters of this sort enlarge knowledge and understanding of materials and product design, and this often leads directly to important safety improvements. It is with these thoughts in mind that we and others have approached the appraisal of the Essex fire. The report by the Connecticut State Fire Marshall deals mostly with aspects concerning the boat yard—the inherent dangers and recommended arrangements, equipment and procedures which will serve to minimize fire risk. The commentary on the fiberglass fuel tanks was not extensive, but the statements were most provocative and consequently commanded attention by the general press and industry publications. For the sake of accuracy and because we wish to discuss and elaborate on the conclusions drawn, we quote from the Fire Marshall's report:

"The investigation developed incidental information which is of interest to this office and may prove signficant in connection with boat safety.

"Although just about all of the metal fuel tanks, both gasoline and diesel, were either ruptured or badly damaged in the fire, the tanks of two of the yachts came through practically unscathed. Both tanks were of fiberglass reinforced plastic construction and were the fuel tanks for two fiberglass craft, both of which (with the exception of the tanks) were totally consumed.

"One of the tanks, of 180-gal. capacity, was three-quarters full of gasoline after the fire. The other tank, of 80-gal. capacity, contained a small amount of gasoline.

"An explanation of this phenomenon could have an important impact on the design of future fuel tank construction and safety tests are being planned at this time. The results may indicate that the thermal insulation value of fiberglass-reinforced plastic fuel tanks may, under fire conditions, be of great value in preventing tank failure and the subsequent release of dangerous fuel to the fire."

Before going further, it is best for us to comment on the fact that there is genuine disagreement by other knowledgeable parties on the

A few yachts outside the shed survived. However, many were set afire when sparks ignited their canvas winter covers.

comparative condition of the metal versus fiberglass tanks found in the wreckage after the fire. It is the view of some that the welded all-metal tanks "held up as expected" and that the "unscathed" description attached to the fiberglass ones was not wholly accurate. But the reinforced plastic tanks drew interest for several reasons. It was startling to see them intact and still containing fuel perched amid the totally burned-out wreckage of their hulls which were constructed of the same basic materials.

Thus the question in the minds of technically interested people is how to explain this phenomenon, if it can be called that. How can a basically combustible material such as glass-reinforced polyester so successfully resist high heat and open flame?

We will leave it to the experts for a final report which probably will be developed on this fire and most particularly on the tanks. However, we feel that by observation and current knowledge that it is quite possible to explain the basic mechanism which took place at the Essex fire.

To be concise, it is believed that there were three to four basic and interacting factors which contributed to the survival of these fiberglass tanks. In the first place, the fiberglass laminate has a low heat conductivity factor particularly as compared to metal. This contributes to a slower rate of vaporization or "boil off" of fuel. It is believed by many that this reduces the danger of internal ignition and explosion. Secondly, as long as fuel remains in the tank, it cools the contacted tank wall to the extent that it will not burn through and dump liquid. This is often called a "tea kettle effect." Directly above the liquid fuel level line, the resin will usually be severely decimated or burned away from the glass reinforcement, depending of course on the intensity and duration of fire exposure. This description fits the tanks in questions. While the upper tank structure still had relatively true form and shape which was due to the stability of the incombustible glass fiber reinforcement, the resin had pretty much been burned out, leaving a material of a charred consistancy not unlike cardboard. Understandably this upper structure was relatively porous and allowed the venting of vaporized gasoline in a manner which probably minimizes the possibility for explosion. In our experience, we have known few fiberglass fuel tanks to suffer internal explosion.

Because of the extent and intensity of the conflagration (the two hulls were located in areas totally enveloped in flame), it is believed that the mounting position of the tanks must have had an important bearing on their survival. The tanks were situated down in the bottom of the deep-V hulls virtually nesting against the hull laminate. Thus, they benefited from the added protection of the hull shell. In contrast, metal tanks have to be mounted up higher to give free air space against the contingencies of corrosion. Coupling this situation with the natural heat conductivity of metal, one can visualize how the flames could more readily surround and "cook" a metal tank. As far as we know, few if any of the metal tanks had liquid gasoline in them after the fire had been extinguished. This has occurred, of course, in other fires of less intensity.

One other position factor undoubtedly came into play in shielding the fiberglass tanks from the enormous heat and flame that were present. As the hulls burned, their structure slumped and settled to the ground, preventing flame from directly reaching the underneath portion and at the same time providing added protection in the glass fiber remains and other carbonized material.

In this regard, it was interesting to note that after the 180 gallon tank had been lifted from the burned-out hull, the hull laminate directly beneath the tank was undamaged and not scorched.

Reducing the foregoing analysis to its essentials, the low heat conductivity and the stabilizing effect from the incombustible glass reinforcements best explain the capability of tanks to resist fire. However, in this case, the position of the tanks in relation to open flame and heat also was a factor of considerable importance.

Adequacy of construction in fuel tanks, regardless of materials, is obviously important to fire resistance. These fiberglass tanks were produced by the Bertram Yacht Co. The 180-gallon tank was installed in their 31' ft. model and the 80-gallon in their 25-footer. Bertram Yacht has been one of the pioneers in constructing fiberglass marine fuel tanks. Over the years they have put a great deal of engineering time into perfecting this equipment, with special emphasis on providing a strong, safe system in compliance with existing standards.

CHAPTER 20

Guide to Judging Hull Structure

HOW CAN YOU EVALUATE the construction of a fiberglass hull? This is a question of interest to a great many individuals who are in the market for new and used glass boats.

Except in the case of the larger, more expensive yachts, a high percentage of the sales transactions are conducted without a detailed survey, or perhaps only a rather casual one. Many buyers choose to judge the craft largely on the basis of builder experience, reputation and obtainable opinions from professionals in the boating business. This is the practical and reliable approach used by the majority of consumers today in the purchase of any complex and expensive item. But the serious boatminded person does seem to require a greater depth of understanding than perhaps is to be found in other fields. A good deal of this is founded in the fact that there are so many different designs and construction variations confronting the prospective purchaser. It is not possible in the following discussion to cover all details and conditions which can come up in a survey. The objective is to suggest a procedure for going over a glass hull which will reveal major shortcomings, and also to discuss some principles of construction. We will try to point out the principal trouble areas and some of the critical design details.

Need to know the fundamentals

If the survey or appraisal to be undertaken is to have any validity, the person must have some knowledge of the basics in glass hull molding. We don't mean a shop knowledge, but an understanding of the way hulls are molded and assembled, the basic mechanics of glass and resin.

In addition, it is very useful to have approximate construction and scantling data on the particular boat in question. By and large the boat builders don't publish this information, but in the case of a new boat it usually can be obtained on request. The type of information that is desirable will become apparent from the discussion which follows.

Exterior hull survey

With the boat out of the water, quite logically, a good beginning point in the inspection procedure is to judge what is readily visible to the eye. First, at a distance, appraise fairness and symmetry of the hull and then move in closer for detail examination.

The usual high gloss finish on a fiberglass hull tends to reveal the slightest discontinuity in the surface, much more than is ordinarily the case with wood or metal hulls. As a consequence, and by the very nature of the material, builders take pains to perfect the surface finish.

While lack of fairness and unbalanced proportions are probably quite rare, detailed aberrations can be found. They are more a matter of demerit than a reasonable cause for rejection. Two examples: the glass weave pattern evident in the glossy surface; or a very slight but visible bulkhead pattern transfer. Such conditions have no bearing on the structural qualities of the hull and should be judged in this light. In the case of a used boat, make sure that there are no cracks or lesions which might be the result of an accident or premature stress failure. Since surface or gel coat cracking and crazing can be found in quite a few older fiberglass boats, be certain to distinguish between this "cosmetic" defect and real structural damage.

It is sufficient to say that true stress cracking, that which is associated with heavy impact or excessive loading, is definitely distinguishable upon close inspection. The crack will penetrate into the reinforced portion of

the laminate, and evidence of its extent will more than likely be visible from the inside.

Due to the ease of repairing a fiberglass hull, relatively small damage should not discourage a prospective owner. It is worthwhile noting, too, that a simple fracture below the waterline where no color matching is required can be a vastly simpler repair proposition than reworking a crazed or pitted topside area.

The monocoque, seamless construction of a fiberglass hull should give permanent insurance against leaks, but this is not always the case, and it is well worthwhile to inspect the few seams or hull penetrations that do exist in any particular hull design. In actual fact, leaks in above-the-deck areas are much more common. This will be discussed subsequently. But faulty joints or seams below the waterline can be serious with any type of hull.

Look closely to see that all through-hull connections, bolted struts, plates, rudder, tubes, etc. are properly seated, sealed and drawn up. Particularly in the case of sailboats with outside ballast, inspect the seam between the deadwood area and the iron or lead. An unwarranted gap between these two elements bears further inspection. Was this caused by grounding? Are the keel bolts started? An inside examination in the affected area is required.

Again in the case of sailboats, give a close inspection to the centerboard slot area for heavy wear or impact. Some small, older centerboards can be of cored fiberglass construction—look for edge wear and distortion. Many sailboats also have cored glass rudders. Considering the trend to the modern spade design, this type should be looked at very closely for adequacy of strength, perhaps not so much in the glass shell fairing as in its supporting metal spider and tube.

Hull thickness—scantlings

Before moving on to a discussion of deck and superstructure, it is appropriate to remark on the matter of laminate scantlings for the hull, and in general.

By and large, pleasure craft are built to construction standards that have been determined by rather pragmatic means—prototype testing and in-use experience, largely backed up by a certain amount of structural testing and stress analysis. In this country at least, for small craft, formal standards are really not used, although Lloyd's and Herreshoff rules may be adhered to on wooden yachts. In consequence the experience and, of course, integrity of the builder are of paramount importance. This is certainly true in fiberglass construction, as much or more so than with traditional materials.

Regardless of the means by which scantlings are arrived at, there are some general principles in fiberglass construction which can be of practical use in the empirical evaluation of a glass hull.

In the industry it is often said that if the fiberglass hull is stiff enough it is strong enough. The technical foundation to this oversimplified statement is that the material, with its high specific strength and resilience, has a low modulus of rigidity. Thus, getting stiffness without adding undue weight or complexity to the structure is a challenge.

The builder will probably use one or a combination of construction methods to achieve panel or section stiffness. He will take advantage of shape, increase shell thickness, employ frame stiffeners, or develop a double skin or sandwich panel. In actual practice today, we see the smallest fiberglass craft utilizing shape and functional parts for stiffness. Sandwich methods are widely used in decks and house tops, and single skin and frame are common for larger hulls.

As far as a survey is concerned, all of this can be reduced to a couple of salient points. One is that even with minimum shell thickness, the points of trouble or failures almost always involve joints, connections or so-called "hard spots." Thus, if you can functionally allow a certain amount of panel deflection in a hull, the real question is how that load is distributed —how it is relieved or taken out at any joint or transition point.

Perhaps a good illustration is the usual thin-wall side of a fiberglass outboard hull. From a functional standpoint, the topside does not have to be as rigid as the flat planing bottom. But how stiff should this section be? Certainly rigid enough to take a rough docking maneuver or

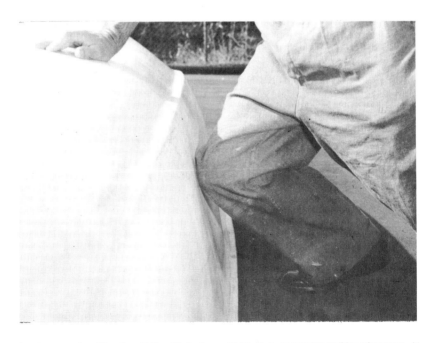

Seamless one-piece fiberglass (left) with its fine molded-in-features presents striking advantages. At the same time the material challenges the industry for better inspection techniques. The "knee" test (right) can be useful at times to appraise the deflection characteristics in the thin wall side of a small hull.

reasonable impact without springing some internal member, or too easily placing the shell in shear stress at a frame or bulkhead.

The fact is, it is difficult to discuss what is minimum shell thickness for any given design, although we feel that general scantling tables for fiberglass will be emerging in the next few years. Experience is the ultimate judge in such a field as this. It is possible, however, to comment on the extremes observed.

Many of the early, larger glass hulls, both power and sail, in the 40-foot range, were built with massively thick bottom panels in the order of three-quarter inch. These early builders were influenced by two factors—conservatism on structure with little or no engineering guidance, and the desire to utilize a simple monocoque structure, solving stiffness by adding thickness.

While there might be a reason to have a build-up of 3/4" in the way of stem, keel or skeg in a sizable hull, it is inefficient and wasteful in the body of the hull. Quite naturally, hulls which have been under-designed with regard to hull laminate thickness have given trouble. For one reason or another, the cases are pretty much confined to small craft below 20 feet. But the interesting fact is that even with a hull which has too light a laminate, failures rarely occur in the clear span area of a panel. This is due to the inherent high resilience of fiberglass. The section usually absorbs an extreme amount of deflection and then breaks at an adjacent hard point, which may be a frame, bulkhead or a shape transition, like a hard chine.

What about test techniques?

A good many people who are familiar with wooden construction, mostly professional builders and surveyors, feel that glass hulls defy critical examination. They think that too much is concealed and is very difficult to judge quantitatively and qualitatively.

We are not at all convinced that this objection to fiberglass construction is reasonable. Not only is the usual unitized structure much simpler, but concern for the types of degradation which wood and metals are prone to are virtually non-existent. Barring any extraordinary abuse or strain, the well-built fiberglass hull appears to have an indefinite life.

Nevertheless there is an interest and a need for a method of accurately determining the substructure of a hull laminate. What would be highly desirable is a simple, portable scanning device which could detect voids, discontinuity and thickness variation. At this time there is no such instrument small enough to be used on a boat hull. It probably will be made available in time. In its absence, surveyors use practical "eyeball" techniques to judge the condition of the hull laminate. A few are worth mentioning.

It is possible to detect voids and general solidity of the laminate by tapping with a hard object. The material is quite dense, more like metal than wood, thus it is possible when tapping to distinguish gradations of thickness, hollow sections and so forth.

Because all but very thick, opaque laminates will transmit light, one

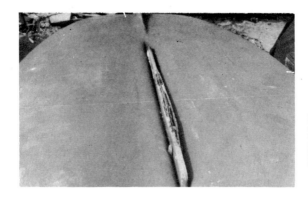

Deteriorated centerboard on small fiberglass catboat. This thin glass lamination over plywood core has been worn away allowing plywood to delaminate.

can actually see a certain amount through shadow and refraction. Ordinarily this is done by having someone pass a bright, electric bulb close to the hull on the outside with the other person observing from the darkened interior. It is sort of a primitive x-ray technique. In actual practice we have found this really only useful for local examination of fracture damage. There are a number of intruding and confusing effects from transmitted light: shadow patterns from thickness variations, fiber patterns, and variations in gel coat density. Interior components may also get in the way.

While it is rare, owners at times have asked for thickness and/or laminate physical property tests on their hulls. To obtain properties such as tensile and flexural strength, a piece perhaps as large as 12 inches square must be cut out and then submitted to a qualified testing laboratory. Such a procedure is often followed in the production of Navy fiberglass hulls, but understandably avoided by commercial builders. Such cutouts involve time and expense which are only justified in very special circumstances.

It is more practical to consider drilling a hole or cutting out a plug to judge thickness, laminate make-up, and glass content. If the holes are judiciously placed, this is not such an objectionable procedure and they are simple to patch and conceal. Any inspection method which involves surgery of any sort is not going to be popular with the boat owner. This reason combined with the fact that it takes some knowledge to interpret the findings has restricted the usage of panel and plug cuts.

It can be readily concluded from the above discussion that the layman is not going to be able to make fine judgments in laminate properties of a given hull. Fortunately, in practice, the common deficiencies are not in the laminate itself, but associated with joints and connections—problem areas which are usually visible or detectable.

Deck-Hull connection & rub rails

As a rule, the deck on a fiberglass hull contributes greatly to the

Sharp impact blows on the bow of this outboard hull reveal a poor laminate. The brittle gel coat breaks away disclosing a dry, porous laminate.

overall stiffness and structural integrity of the boat. This means that the connection between the hull and deck must be strong and reliable. Second in importance is that the joint be completely watertight.

Builders usually make this joint by bonding with strips of fiberglass, possibly assisted by mechanical fasteners. Any one of a number of methods is used, depending on the joint design selected, sheer configuration, rub rail hardware, and so forth. Some recent small boat designs have gone completely to mechanically fastened joints. This appeals to us because the deck can be more easily removed if major repairs are ever necessary. However, watertightness will be entirely dependent on some sort of flexible sealant.

An interior inspection of this area in the boat will reveal the construction method, and major flaws are not hard to detect. If lack of watertightness is suspected, a well-aimed stream of water sprayed along the sheer will confirm it.

Until recent years, many rub rail installations, particularly on outboard boats, were of poor design and materials. They could be too easily distorted or loosened and were hard to fasten back in place. The types in question are extruded vinyl or synthetic rubber held in place by tension and adhesive, and the aluminum extruded assembly which may or may not incorporate a pop-out rubber strip. Although not structural, a well-designed rub rail not only enhances the appearance of a boat but gives sound protection in a vulnerable area. It should be strong, abuse-resistant and relatively simple to replace or repair.

The Deck Areas

There is nothing more disconcerting than to hop off the dock onto a bouncy, highly polished fiberglass deck which happens to be wet. Disaster is assured because the deck will be very slippery and unstable. By exaggeration we are trying to make two points. One is that working areas must have an effective anti-skid treatment, and secondly, fiberglass decks should be firm and unyielding. Many builders of small and some large craft elect not to provide an anti-skid finish, leaving it to the owner to apply pressure-sensitive traction strips or anti-skid paint. No matter what system is used, security under foot is essential to safety.

Flexible or bouncy fiberglass decks are now pretty much a matter of the past since builders have developed better stiffening techniques. But it is useful to understand the construction of the deck on any particular glass boat in order to properly mount fittings and accessories. Sandwich core methods are commonly used for big, clear-span decks. Carling-type stiffeners of glass or wood are more often used to support decks of outboard boat size.

A variety of core materials are employed in sandwich deck panels—balsa, plywood and several types of plastic foams. Balsa is perhaps the most popular currently with the builders. In any case, the type of core, its arrangement and possibly the thickness can usually be determined by a close underdeck inspection. If a heavily-loaded fitting or accessory is to be mounted on a balsa or foam core deck, be sure to get some knowledgeable advice on the correct method of attaching it. These materials have no screw-holding power and will crush and shear under high local compression.

Fiberglass decks offer the minimum possibility for leaks, but in any sizable craft, there are a multitude of penetrations—fittings, hatches, dead lights, port lights and so forth. Leaks therefore can be due to imperfect seals between the laminate and fixture or possibly poor closure fit in an assembly such as a motorboat window. Small, annoying leaks sometimes will originate from less conspicuous fittings such as stanchion bases or chain plate ears. Close inspection of all such mountings which penetrate the deck and superstructure (again, if possible, assisted by the water hose test) is well worthwhile.

Interior Hull Structure

Survey of the interior hull structure can involve a host of elements and, of course, many variations from one type of craft to another. It is only possible here to try and discuss some of the major and common features.

If it is true that the smooth, uninterrupted outside of the hull shell tends to conceal the nature of the structure, quite the opposite is the case from the inside. Not only are the structural details quite well displayed, but because of the "outside-in" laminating sequence, a judgment of some value can be made by studying the lay-up technique.

Most hulls are produced in a cavity mold using the contact molding system. This results in a smooth exterior finish and a relatively rough or coarse interior. There can be a definite correlation between neatness and precision of this visible laminate and the quality of the portion which cannot be seen. Sloppy joints, excessive accumulations of resins, resin-starved areas and general unevenness of the laminate do not suggest care and know-how.

Only the smallest fiberglass hulls rely entirely on the hull shell for strength and stiffness. Even these designs often employ some functional part such as a box seat or molded floor as a support member. A few craft like the ubiquitous Boston Whaler have a fully developed sandwich core that provides the needed overall rigidity. But more common is a combination of longitudinal stiffeners and transverse bulkheads. These members are joined to the hull shell with strips of fiberglass and resin. In some small hulls connection is made entirely with a bonding putty. In any case these joints should be subjected to close inspection. Be alert for cracking and delamination of these secondary bonds. In powerboats the longitudinal stringers are critical load-bearing, bottom-stiffening members, which often also serve as the foundation for the engines. Heavy power plants impart torsion, virbration and high inertial impact loads to a hull.

Sailboats have less need for longitudinal stiffeners due to their general hull form and lower speeds. However, certain areas in the fore body can be exposed to heavy slamming and may require extra reinforcement to prevent oil-canning of the hull shell.

Transverse stiffening requirements seem to be less of a factor. From experience to date it seems that the monocoque shell incorporating property designed stringers combined with a well-developed sheer and deck assembly, needs little additional lateral support.

Each type of boat has her own particularly highly stressed areas which require special inspection, and it is not difficult to determine these areas after familiarization and study. We offer the survey outline included in this discussion as a guide and also recommend the "Gibbs & Cox Survey Manual" for more detailed directions.

Problem of Concealed Construction

There are some practices used in the design and construction of fiberglass hulls which make inspection difficult. They have to do with the fact that it is sometimes impossible to gain access to an area for inspection or that a key member is encased in fiberglass.

In the first situation, an example would be an extensive molded interior behind which are located structural or mechanical elements that need examination. For instance, many of the early fiberglass outboards incorporated wooden stringers topped off with a glassed-over plywood floor. There is no way to inspect this area short of cutting through the floor panel. Certainly if such an older hull proves to have a yielding, spongy floor, a section will have to be cut out to gain access. The point can also be made that if wooden structural members are to be incorporated, it is quite important to be able to get to and inspect them periodically.

QUESTIONNAIRE
Fiberglass Reinforced Plastics Boat and Vessel Construction Data

IDENTIFICATION:
Type or Class
Builder
Designer
Year Built
Principal Characteristics:

LOA	Design Displacement
LWL	Cubic Footage
Beam	Ballast Weight
Depth	Horsepower:
Draft	Inboard
Freeboard	Outboard
Weight (net shipping)	Speed—Maximum

BOAT CONSTRUCTION DATA:
Basic Materials:
Resin
Polyester
Epoxy
Other (Specify)
Reinforcement—Refer to tables
Core—Refer to Tables
Finish: Gel Coat ☐ Paint ☐ Other (Specify)
Molding:
Mold: Female ☐ Male ☐ Other (Specify)
Method: Contact ☐ Other (Specify)

SYMBOLS	
Use these symbols in following tables for Types of Reinforcement	**M** = Mat **S** = Spray-up **WR** = Woven Roving **C** = Cloth **X** = Other

LAMINATES—NOMINAL

	Single Skin		Sandwich						
			Outer Skin		Core			Inner Skin	
	Reinf. No. of Plies, Type & Weight	Nominal Thickness	Reinf. No. of Plies, Type & Weight	Nominal Thickness	Type	Nominal Thickness	Density	Reinf. No. of Plies, Type & Weight	Nominal Thickness
Hull									
Bottom									
Side									
Transom									
Other									
(Specify)									
Decks									
Deck									
Cabin Top									
Cockpit									
Other									
(Specify)									
Structural Bulkheads									

Designers and builders are now much more conscious of this inspection problem and provide for it in better arrangement and detailing.

The matter of encasing other materials in a laminate is a broad

a Hull Survey
A Structural Survey

					—Width, inches
			Depth, inches		
FRAMING—NOMINAL					
		Stiffener			
Location	Core Material	Depth	Width	Spacing Inches	Reinforcement No. of Plies, Type & Weight
Hull					
Bottom					
Sides					
Transom					
Other					
(Specify)					
Decks					
Deck					
Cabin Top					
Cockpit					
Other					
(Specify)					
Structural					
Bulkheads					

	Use symbols for indication in tables	
CONNECTION AND ATTACHMENTS		
Location	Secondary Bond Type & No. of Plies of Reinforcement	Fasteners Type & Spacing
Hull		
One-piece Hull—Check ☐	Not Applicable	Not Applicable
Shell Halves		
Other		
Decks		
Deck to Hull Side (Sketch)		
Cabin Top to Sides		
Cabin Sole		
Cockpit		
Other		
Bulkheads		
Bulkhead to Shell		
Bulkhead to Decks		
Miscellaneous (Sketches Preferred)		
Engine Foundation		
Mast Step		
Chain Plates		
Ballast		
Center Board Trunk		
Other		

subject and cannot be dealt with thoroughly in this discussion. The "Gibbs & Cox Survey Manual" does have a well organized section on this. However, for the purposes of guidance here we are more interested in how to determine soundness of construction than in judging what materials should or should not be encased. Experience has shown that a wide variety of materials have been encased locally and extensively with little or no difficulty. It has been demonstrated rather clearly that the proper technique and an understanding of the properties of the particular material determine success or failure.

Incorporation of wood in a hull laminate is a commonly observed practice. Plywood and balsa are considered to be the most trouble-free from the standpoint of expansion and contraction. Hardwoods like oak have given the poorest experience due to propensity to expand and to bond poorly. At any rate, one will observe plywood cores used extensively in the strengthening and stiffening of outboard transoms—plywood and fir are often glassed over for stringers in a powerboat hull. A balsa sandwich bottom will also be found in some power hulls, and we know of at least one outboard builder who has used core sheets of plywood in the bottom of his hulls for some years.

The general trend in new fiberglass boats, however, is away from incorporation and encasement of organic materials in the hull and particularly below the waterline. To some degree, largely in small craft, foam cores have been substituted.

From a survey standpoint, one should find out where wood inclusions are present in the hull laminate and then determine if the area is sound and strong. Tapping with a coin or metal instrument can be helpful in detecting any bond separation. By drilling small holes or taking plug cuts it is possible to ascertain whether water has penetrated and, of course, whether rot may have set in.

CHAPTER 21

Construction Projects

BUILDING A FIBERGLASS PRAM

MANY BOAT OWNERS have indicated great interest in building their own fiberglass boat or some associated component. A high percentage of people who participate in this sport enjoy, and are accustomed to, doing major as well as minor construction work. This inclination is founded as much on the pure satisfaction of self-accomplishment as on any economic savings which result.

Steel and aluminum are not materials which the average amateur can easily work with to develop any complex structure, such as a hull. Wood, in its various forms, does adapt itself well to home shop construction. In addition, the rudiments of woodworking are generally acquired early in life if the individual has any mechanical bent.

Fiberglass materials, on the other hand, have only come recently on the scene. Developments in their usage have outpaced the written word. While they do adapt well to home shop work, there are peculiarities and limitations which must be well understood to work out a successful project.

Frankly, the fiberglass industry has not been too anxious to encourage or promote amateur boat construction. During the 1950's the expanding outboard industry was plagued with too many backyard shops putting together fiberglass boats which did not reflect well on the material. The situation being what it was, we were a bit sensitive on the subject of home shop construction. We attempted to divert the ambitious amateur towards purchasing a well-built glass boat which we were sure would give satisfaction.

However, we do respect the fact that many boatmen have a serious desire to construct their own boats. To this must be added that many amateurs are top-notch craftsmen and have the initiative and ability to complete successfully large, complex projects. Indeed, some of the important contributions have come from basement and backyard shops.

The dinghy molding project described here is gauged to appeal to the man of average mechanical skills, who wants to profitably spend a reasonable number of winter hours on a worthwhile project. As to estimating the experience necessary, it can be put in this frame of reference. With the method proposed there will be less skill and labor required than in the building of an equivalent eight-foot plywood pram. The writer has done both. Secondly, if you have had experience covering a wooden hull or deck with resin and fiberglass cloth, you have all the necessary fiberglassing skill to do this job. The molding methods described herein are simply an elaboration of the rather well-known fiberglass covering technique.

The Mold

The dinghy mold can be developed in any number of ways. But mold-making is an art in itself. A really good mold is a great deal of work, probably beyond the interest of any but the most ambitious amateur. To minimize the work in this phase we suggest that an old wooden pram be used as the mold. We urge you to use an old, discarded boat for two reasons. Number one, it is necessary to remove rails and other projecting members so that the glass shell will easily detach itself. Secondly, because the glass lamination shrinks slightly, the wooden boat may take quite a lot of abuse in the process of cracking the cured fiberglass shell from its male counterpart.

The hard-chined pram shown in this article was molded over an old plywood model which was no longer serviceable. To convert it to a good mold we performed the following:

1. Removal of outer gunwale, skeg, bang strips and so on. We left the outer keel in place because it held the hull together structurally.

2. All corners were chamfered with sandpaper to quarter-inch radius. The keel was rounded too and a fillet of plastic wood built up at the garboard so that the glass would form easily.

3. Screw holes and cracks were filled with plastic wood and the surface sanded fair. Because we were not too concerned with a perfect finish, we simply applied two heavy coats of paint so that the wood was sealed properly.

4. The final step in mold preparation involved three polished coats of Johnson's paste wax and a brush coat of a parting film. The parting film is readily available from any plastics supply house. It is basically a polyvinyl alcohol film in liquid form, soluble in water.

Molding Materials

As in any artisan trade, good fiberglass work requires the perfection of technique developed from experience. The problem of the do-it-yourself mechanic, however, is that he wishes to achieve acceptable results on his first try. The suggestions here on materials and methods are aimed to insure this measure of success; they are not necessarily guaranteed to direct him towards the fastest and least expensive procedure.

The basic fiberglass material suggested for this dinghy molding project is a standard weight "boat cloth," weighing about ten-ounces per yard with an open, square weave. It is readily available at retail marine stores. This cloth has good strength and body, wets out easily, and conforms nicely to any shape. The weave is fine enough so that a good outside surface can be arrived at with minimum effort. Production-

Mold ready for application of glass and resin. All exterior trim has been removed.

Fiberglass hull shell after removal from mold.

molded boats utilize the coarser fabric (woven roving), but this material is not recommended for use by amateurs.

Use polyester type resin. We suggest the standard boat-covering formulation which cures tack-free at room temperature. This resin contains a filler to prevent resin drainage and a wax agent which insures a non-sticky surface after it has turned from liquid to solid. Because of the wax agent, however, you must sand thoroughly between successive cured laminations to insure a good bond.

Molding Procedure

The small pram pictured in this article required four layers of ten-ounce cloth in the bottom and three layers in the sides and transoms. Because the keel area and all corners were inherently high-stress points, we overlapped the cloth panels generously so that we have the equivalent of six layers in the keel and garboard area and a minimum of four at the sharp transom corners.

205

Each different design will require a slightly different lay-up sequence, but if the principle is understood and the procedure planned out ahead of time, no problems should be encountered. On this typical square-ended pram it was simplest to start by laying up a layer of cloth on the transom panels first. carrying a two-inch overlap onto the bottom. Then each side of the bottom received a layer of cloth, doubling up at the keel. Before adding the next series of cloth panels, rough spots and edges were sanded down. The whole cured surface area required a brisk rough sanding to insure proper bond with successive laminations.

The technique of lay-up may seem a bit awkward and messy at first, but one of the very good features of the materials is that any mistake can be corrected. The hardened lamination can be easily cut and reshaped with a disc grinder or file. The material machines much like a soft metal. Another important point is that the lay-up operation can be stopped at almost any point and resumed at any time.

Concerning The Plaid Topsides

The novel effect on the sides of the pram were achieved by laminating a layer of tartan plaid cotton cloth over the final ply of glass cloth. The finished effect is rather startling, because the thin-walled laminate is quite translucent. The treatment successfully used on this little boat undoubtedly will suggest any number of ideas to the reader. The colors in the plaid, after four seasons, did eventually fade to the point that painting was required. One suggestion, if you do decide to "mold in" some special effect, do make some test samples to check the adhesion and general compatibility of the resin with the "patterned" material.

Left—Cotton plaid fabric has been laminated to sides and transom. Mahogany gun'ls and transom plates are major stiffening members. Note skeg molded to keel. Right— Eight-foot fiberglass pram molded over an old Hagerty Sea Shell. Novel topsides pattern created by layer of tartan plaid cloth.

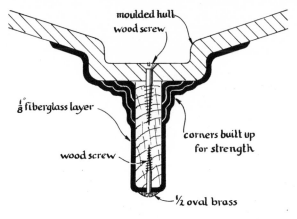

moulded hull

wood screw

⅛" fiberglass layer

wood screw

corners built up for strength

½ oval brass

Diagram of building of the skeg.

Release From The Mold

Removing the glass shell from the mold will be a point of some anticipation and excitement. The whole operation may seem a little uncertain up to this point—perhaps like a bride baking her first cake. A soft-head mallet or similar instrument should be used to break the bond between the cured glass lamination and the mold form. A round-edged metal pry bar can be effective in levering the shell free. The glass molding will submit to quite a lot of working without damage, but the mold may be damaged in the process. This is one reason we suggest using an old boat for a form.

Structural Stiffeners And Finishing

After removal from the mold, the hull shell will have the rough appearance of a boat, but it is in actual fact only half complete and will be very limber. The succeeding steps described herein are vital. The detailed assembly and stiffening techniques advanced here can obviously be varied but we urge the interested reader to study thoroughly the basic principles involved.

Mahogany Gunwales

The first step on completion of the molded shell was to install wooden gunwales, sandwiching the laminate in between. They were drawn together with bronze screws. We used 1¼" x 5/8" stock.

Transom Plates

To stiffen the transoms we glued, with epoxy cement, mahogany plates to the inside of the bow and stern transoms.

207

Fiberglass Corner Braces

In order to link the gunwales and the transom plates together we installed flat fiberglass braces, laminated with six layers of cloth and then cut to shape. They were screw-fastened to the wooden member.

Skeg

The skeg was built by first shaping a soft pine member to proper dimensions and screw-fastening it into position. We then molded about a 1/8″ of glass over the wood, lapping it onto the hull. Because this glass lamination would suffer from abrasion, we attached a bronze bang strip to the skeg.

Seats

The fore-and-aft seats are fiberglass box chambers. By their shape they considerably stiffen the bottom and sides. Wedged under them are blocks of Styrofoam for flotation. A hole at the bottom permits water to drain out. Since air-tight chambers are difficult for the amateur to develop, we suggest this system.

The fore-and-aft seats were molded over a Masonite form, using five layers of cloth, and bonded in place with mat and resin.

The center thwart is mahogany and suspended by bronze brackets from the gunwale. Because the side wall laminate was thin we were careful to not let the butt ends of the thwart meet the sides and cause a hard spot. The thwart is securely bolted to the rigid gunwale but floats free from the thin sides.

The prop under the mid-thwart is fiberglassed to the hull shell with mat and tape. The area immediately under and adjacent to the foot of the prop was reinforced with fiberglass to distribute properly any unusual loads.

The dinghy described herein has been in constant service, winter and summer, for many years now. Other than the varnish work and the more recent need for a coat of epoxy paint over the faded plaid topsides she has required no special repairs. In the overall the boat cost about 20 percent more than a plywood kit pram.

BUILDING AN INTEGRAL WATER TANK

AS THE NUMBER of fiberglass boats has grown, there has been an increase in questions regarding alterations and additions which can be carried out by the owner. One of the questions which comes up quite often is the matter of installing a fiberglass water tank.

We believe that this is a project well within the capabilities of the average boat owner. Due to the design freedom provided by fiberglass materials there are any number of ways in which tanks can be worked out and we would now like to discuss, and in some detail, an approach which is probably the simplest, is quite broadly applicable, and is suggestive of good technique for other, similar modifications to a molded glass hull.

The tank design described herein is the integral type. It is considered simpler to do for the amateur than the separate type because no molds are needed, joints are kept to a minimum, and less laminating is required.

Consider Effect On Trim And Stability

The integral tank probably makes most sense where one is utilizing at least two existing hull surfaces for the tank walls. A clearer idea of this reasoning will be apparent as the fabrication techniques are described. The accompanying sketch shows an integral, bow tank installation. Its location as shown is a practical one, but it is not necessarily proper for all designs. The owner must analyze what the weight of water will do to the trim of the craft and to her general stability. Hence the advice of a naval architect may be required. Remember that water weighs over eight-pounds per gallon and an 18-gallon tank in the forepeak can simulate the weight of a man standing on the foredeck.

If, for example, the tank as shown in the sketch is too far forward for proper trim, it may be possible to locate it farther aft to reduce the weight moment. A dam wall can be erected at the forward end, just as is shown in the after end. It would, of course, then be advisable to provide a limber tube for draining any water which might accumulate forward of the tank. This can be done by molding a small tube of plastic or metal into the bottom of the tank.

General Location Possibilities

For the owner interested in such a project, it would prove well worthwhile to examine tank arrangements in other fiberglass boats. Integral water tanks are commonly seen in glass auxiliaries and in some glass power cruisers. In the case of sailboats, it is quite the usual thing to see the tank located above the ballast, below the cabin sole. This makes good use of space and puts the weight amidships and at the lowest point in the hull. In fiberglass power boats, integral tanks are often developed between the longitudinal glass stringers and the hull shell. Locations are usually amidships or forward.

Principles Of Construction

The general idea of the proposed system is to enclose the selected area with prefabricated fiberglass panels, using glass and resin to bond the formed panels to the existing structure. The panels are laminated and cut to approximate fit in the workshop. Hardware is also mounted before installation, which is much simpler than trying to do this work within the confines of the hull. The erection of the tank in the boat merely involves fiberglassing these panels to the shell.

The question might be raised about using plywood panels instead of fiberglass and simply lining the inside of the tank compartment with glass cloth and resin. This system can be used and apparently has been done successfully, but we feel that exclusion of wood will make longer-lasting, trouble-free installation.

The question of using ready-made fiberglass flat panels might also be raised. Such material can certainly serve the purpose, but it will probably be difficult for the average individual to obtain the thickness required.

Molding Materials

The necessary glass reinforcing materials can be reduced to two or three items. The panels should be sandwich buildup of 1½-ounce chopped strand mat and regular ten-ounce boat cloth. The mat is used to aid in getting thickness, but it also insures against any pin-hole leaks. Four or six-inch wide boat type will come in handy for bonding the panels in place.

Polyester resin widely sold at retail for fiberglassing wooden boats will be satisfactory. Color pigment is probably not required as the natural clarity of the resin may prove advantageous in that the water level can be seen through a tank wall which is unpigmented.

A polyvinyl alcohol film or sheet of cellophane may prove useful as a separating film when laying up the panels. An ordinary paste wax will serve the same purpose, but you must be careful and thorough about removing the wax from the laminated panel when making subsequent bonds. The forms on which the glass panels will be laid up can be Masonite, plywood or any stiff, flat material which is easily workable with hand tools.

How To Proceed

1. Thoroughly clean the entire hull area which comprises the tank. With a power sander grind away dirt, surface paint, etc.

2. When using Masonite or plywood material, first establish the

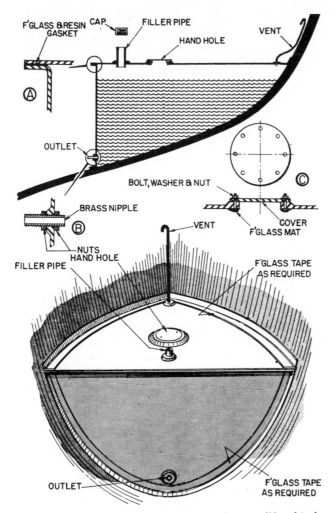

Construction details (A), bonded connection between lid and tank wall. (B), detail of water line connection. (C), fiberglass clean-out plate assembly.

dimension and position of the after dam wall. This is best done on a "cut and fit" basis. It does not have to be done with extreme accuracy as any small gaps can be filled with glass and resin when the actual molded panel is erected.

3. The flat template is next used as form on which to laminate the glass panel. In order to get the flange at the top it may be necessary to tack an extra piece of wood along this edge. Apply wax or separating film to the template so that the resin will not stick.

4. Cut glass mat and cloth to the approximate size of the template leaving an eighth to a quarter-inch overage at the perimeter. This flash can be easily ground off after the laminate has hardened.

5. Lay up alternate plies (cloth-mat-cloth) until the desired thickness is achieved. Don't try to impregnate too much glass at one time. Two layers of cloth with mat in between is probably the maximum. Use the cloth as a kind of screen to impregnate the loose fiber mat. When applying more laminations to cured material, sand the cured surface thoroughly first to insure a good bond.

The actual thickness of the tank wall is to a large degree a matter of judgment. For the small tanks under consideration here we would recommend this sequence, 10 oz. cloth - 1½ oz. mat - 10 oz. cloth - 1½ oz. mat - 10 oz. cloth. This will result in about .150″ minimum wall or just under three-sixteenths. In any case, one-eighth should be considered a bare minimum for any tank wall.

If time or impregnation difficulties do not permit a "full" thickness lay-up before cure, it is entirely practical to let the work done harden and then come back at any time later and add more glass and resin. The only "must" is that the old surface should be thoroughly sanded. If this requirement is fulfilled, a good secondary bond will be established.

6. When the above "dam wall" is finished, trim off the excess flash on the edges with a disk grinder and establish a reasonably close fit in the hull. Gaps up to an eighth of an inch are permissible.

7. Before the panel is installed, a brass feed line fitting should be installed in a position as shown in the accompanying sketch. When thin tank walls are involved (1/8 inch) a boss of fiberglass and resin twice the thickness should be built up around the fitting, perhaps to an extent of twice the diameter of the fitting. Take-up nuts and washers should be used on both sides of the tank wall. A rigid epoxy cement seal or flexible compound can be used under the washers.

8. The "dam wall" is then bonded in place. Use fiberglass mat and fiberglass tape. The mat strip goes on first and then the tape. Bond both sides of the panel to the hull for maximum strength. A two-inch overlap is adequate. The contact surfaces should be clean, dry and sanded.

9. Fabrication of the tank top is identical to that of the wall plate with the exception of certain hardware details. A clean-out access cover plate is highly desirable. This can be provided by conventional deck plate fittings of hand hole size with a screw cover; the assembly can be epoxy bonded in place. Less expensive is a plate made of fiberglass which is held in place by bolts and sealed with a rubber gasket. The bolts should be bedded and sealed in a lamination of fiberglass and resin to prevent them from turning when the nuts are drawn up tight. Extra securance of the bolt heads can be provided by drilling the bolt heads through and running lock pins through the holes.

A fill fitting should be provided and a small pressure relief tube. The latter should run up towards the sheer and hook over so that water forced out will drain away to the bilges. The fill fitting can be incorporated into the cleanout cover plate or it may be separate.

Bosses should be provided for all above fittings. According to commercial marine codes, clean-out plates should be raised to a height that will prevent dirt from falling into the tank when the cover is removed.

10. When the tank lid and its fittings are assembled, it can be installed in the boat using the same bonding technique as previously described in connection with aft wall.

Before the lid goes on, clean out the tank area once more. Grind off all loose material and vacuum clean the chamber. Fit the lid in place and bond with strips of mat and tape. Connection with the aft flange can be implemented with a gasket of resin-saturated mat. Rig up clamps to hold the joint or perhaps use sheet metal screws.

11. The tank is now essentially complete, but two more steps are still necessary. First, pressure test the tank for leaks with air or water pressure. Second, to prevent possible taste from the polyester resin, steam the tank for a couple of hours. The steaming will purge the laminate of excess styrene which lingers in a freshly layed up laminated tank. Any jury rig steam device will suffice for this function.

Baffles

There are no precise regulations on the need for baffles in water tanks. The 15-gallon bow tank which has been described does not need a slosh baffle, but for larger types one would be recommended. Here again we would suggest a glass laminate bonded to the sides and bottom of the tank with holes positioned to provide free passage of fluid.

BUILDING A PLASTIC ICEBOX

CRUISING COMFORT can be greatly improved by having on board a well-built, efficient icebox. If your boat is not so equipped, it is possible to add this convenience in a number of ways. Many of the larger, modern power cruisers have electric refrigeration units which are generally small-sized household units. Such power craft have the necessary electric system and quite often the motorboat has the space to accept the bulk of a small standard refrigerator.

But the regular shore-side refrigerator or the many portable icebox designs that are available are not very adaptable to the interior arrangement of small cruising sail or motor boats. The best answer is a built-in icebox which is conveniently located and makes maximum utilization of space. Such units are widely seen in modern cruising sailboats. A great many of these iceboxes are constructed from glass-plastic materials.

By virtue of the characteristics of these modern materials we feel it entirely practical for an amateur to fabricate a box for his own boat. The following will endeavor to provide guidance for such a project.

Old And New Methods

It isn't too long ago that yacht iceboxes were constructed of metal liners with wood outer sheathing and cabinetry. Insulation might have been such natural substances as cork, balsa or low-density fiber board.

Today we are offered a better selection of materials, both from the standpoint of simplified fabrication and improved thermal efficiency. The metal liner is replaced by plastic which is non-corrosive, easier to keep clean and has low thermal conductivity. Modern insulation in the form of mineral wool, glass fiber or foamed plastic are light non-absorbent and highly effective barriers to heat and cold.

As many readers may know, mass-produced refrigerators such as those for household use are equipped with many internal plastic components including the entire inner liner shell. These plastic materials are generally of the thermo-plastic variety—not fiberglass reinforced. The thermoplastic types are adequately strong for this non-structural application and they can be provided at less cost and at a high rate of production from big, expensive injection molding machines. But the volume must be present to justify such tooling. Such volume doesn't exist in the boat business, so we turn to fiberglass-plastic construction that can be developed from low-cost forms.

Suggested Construction Method

Considering the range and flexibility of materials offered today, there are any number of ways to build a good icebox. However, we prefer this basic technique. The system provides a smooth, durable inner fiberglass shell

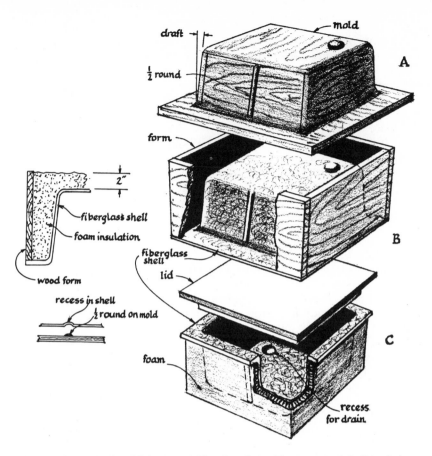

(A) Wooden mold for fabrication of fiberglass liner. Three per cent draft angle to facilitate release of part. Half-round creates recess to accept baffle. (B) Lightly fastened restraining fixture used for foaming operation. (C) If need be, foam can be sheathed with glass cloth and polyester resin. Wooden lid satisfactory—insulation considered optional.

enclosed by highly efficient insulation of foamed plastic. The exact technique of handling fiberglass and resin will not be thoroughly treated here because we feel that for this icebox project the amateur should have some primary training in handling the materials. If you have covered a deck or hull with fiberglass this job will be no more difficult.

The use of a male mold may seem like extra work to some individuals. It is, of course, possible to develop the box out of panels of foam plastic or perhaps balsa and then sheathe the inside and outside with glass and resin. But in the end there is almost as much labor involved, due to fitting and finishing. The recommended method, carefully done, will yield professional results.

The only "trick" part of this project, which may be new to many home shop craftsmen, is the use of "foam-in-place" plastic for the insulation component. It would be possible to use glass or mineral wool insulation or to glue preformed panels of foam to the liner shell. But these materials are less adaptable to irregular contours that are generally involved with built-in ice chests. We have found the "foam-in-place" kits very simple to use. You merely mix two liquid components together and pour into a cavity where it will expand in a yeast-like fashion, filling all the space.

The accompanying drawings are submitted as illustrations of principles and procedures rather than detailed specifications. The interested craftsman may want to introduce variations in design and hardware detail. The sketches show a simple, rectangular, toploader type box with removable lid. However, the construction method would only be slightly modified to take care of a front-loader.

Construction Procedure

The first step is to fabricate a properly dimensioned form over which the fiberglass inner liner is molded. Considering the simple shape shown in the drawing, tempered Masonite or plywood panels can be used for the flat areas. The rounded corners are best developed by rabbeting the panels into pieces of soft white pine that can be shaped to a generous radius. The rounded corners facilitate molding and provide for easier cleaning of the icebox. Sculptor's wax can be used to develop a proper radius at the flange and for a build-up where the drain is to be located.

Before laminating can start, the form must be worked to a smooth, even finish and a release agent applied. The latter is accomplished by several rubbed coats of ordinary paste wax and a brushed-on application of parting film (usually polyvinyl alcohol, under various trade names).

The mold is now ready for laminating. A smooth white interior of the box shell is best provided by a gel coat of polyester resin. This special formulation can be purchased from a plastic supply house along with the regular laminating polyester resin.

After the gel coat is dry, application of the fiberglass can begin. It is suggested that a standard ten-ounce boat cloth will be the easiest and most satisfactory to use throughout this project. The number of layers should be determined and cut roughly to size. Program the lay-up of these layers according to your experience and the nature of the mold form.

With regard to the number of plies and thicknesses needed, advice has to be general because of the variable involved. If uncertainty prevails, make up some small "bench" samples of different thicknesses to get the feel of the material. While stiffness is always a major consideration with fiberglass construction, remember that shape and back-up reinforcement can assist greatly. In this case the foam envelope will introduce tremendous over-all rigidity. Considering the size box indicated here, it would seem that a minimum of two layers could be used in the sides and three or four on the bottom. The flange lip, which will probably be used as mounting point, should be increased to four or five layers.

After cure, the fiberglass shell should be removed from the mold before proceeding with the foaming operation. Note in the drawing that a slight draft angle has been indicated in the design of the mold so that the part will slip free properly. In home shop work, where relatively crude plugs or forms are developed, it is not uncommon to have the fiberglass part stick and become difficult to separate. However, since the project is a "one off" operation, dismemberment of the male plug is practical and simple to do if it has not been fastened too securely.

After the shell has been taken from its form, the next step is to prepare it for foam incasement. The technique suggested involves placing the liner, open end down, on a wood base; then erect a restraining fixture around the sides, leaving the top fully open for pouring the foam. The distance of the restraining panels from the shell, of course, determines the insulation thickness. A thickness of about two inches will be quite adequate. In order to remove the panels after the foam has set, it is necessary to cover them with a plastic film like Saran wrap. The foam adheres quite tenaciously to metal, wool and fiberglass.

Small packaged quantitites of the "foam-in-place" polyurethane plastic are available from many plastic supply houses. The brand we have used successfully was furnished by Glass Plastics Corp., 1605 West Elizabeth Avenue, Linden, N.J. A quart kit of two pint cans will make one and a half cubic feet. It is more expensive than Styrofoam or glass insulation, but, has decided advantages.

The contents of the two cans are mixed in equal parts in a clean open container and then poured almost immediately into the cavity. Temperature control is important. The operation should be conducted above 70 degrees and it may be necessary to insure that the cavity is at least up to this temperature by providing auxiliary heat. Unless this precaution is taken the foam will not expand to its proper volume before setting, and thereby unnecessary waste is incurred. It is best to under-foam a cavity and come back with a second or third mix. Fresh foam will bond very nicely to previously poured quantities. Excess at the top can be easily trimmed with a saw or knife.

After the restraining panels are removed it may be desirable to protect the foam by covering it with a layer or two of glass cloth. The need for this would depend on how the box is to be mounted. In some installations the foam might not be subject to any abuse.

The top of the icebox might be built in any number of ways. For one thing, it is probably not as important to insulate the lid as it would be the door of a front loader. A solid wooden lid that fits snugly will keep the cold in effectively. There are a variety of household weatherstripping seals that can be applied to the lid. If it does seem advisable to insulate the wooden lid, consider this technique. Obtain a piece of polyurethane foam. Cut this to size and cover with several layers of fiberglass cloth and resin leaving a flange at the edge in order to screw-fasten the piece to the under side of the lid. If you select Styrofoam for the job, use epoxy laminating resin rather than a polyester. The latter type resin will unfortunately dissolve Styrofoam, but it has no effect on polyurethane foam.

MOLDING A UTILITY BOX OR PAN

SIMPLE MOLDS can be quickly and inexpensively developed for use in the fabrication of small, functional boat applications. For illustration we have selected the basic form of a box or pan. There are many uses around a boat for a specially-fabricated shape of this nature in fiberglass, like the following examples:

A box to contain wet-cell storage batteries molded out of fiberglass polyester laminate, will be durable, light, and immune to damage from spilled acid.

A crankcase drip pan can be as easily fabricated in fiberglass as the usual metal counterpart. The formability of fiberglass will provide detailing of shape that better fits irregular areas under the engine.

Utility boxes or drawers for storage of tools or other articles will be tough, resistant to stain or rust, and easier to keep clean.

Fish or bait boxes are obviously good applications for fiberglass. The smooth, non-absorbent surface is easy to keep clean and odor-free. Such boxes in fiberglass are being offered for sale by several companies.

In a sense, a hatch cover is an inverted box or shallow pan. At least for the purposes of this discussion, it can be so considered. A hatch cover in glass has a number of potential advantages over standard wood construction. It will require less maintenance, will not expand or contract—can be stronger and lighter. If desirable, the laminate can be made translucent. Molds of many types and materials construction are used in reinforced plastics. Because of the versatility of wood and the fact that at least rudimentary skills in its usage are almost universal, wooden molds are popular for "one off" projects. Considering the simple, box-shaped parts under discussion here, the wood forms are best. Necessary wood materials are readily available at low cost. Two basic, wood mold forms are suggested—the cavity type and the plug or male, form. In the one case you are laminating inside the form; in the second, laminating the glass over the outside of the form.

The cavity mold is used most often when producing a repetitive number of contact molded parts like boat hulls. However, for the "one off" home shop project, it is not necessary to be bound to this system. The mold form selected by the amateur should be the type that is easiest for him to handle and consistent with his capabilities in working with glass-plastic materials. The reasoning behind this statement will become clearer as we go on.

As a basic principal, the cavity mold should be employed where a smooth outside surface is desired, and the plug or male mold used when the best surface is required on the inside. For example, a drawer or bait box requires a smooth even surface on the inside, therefore they are perhaps best molded over a plug. A hatch cover, on the other hand, needs its best surface on the outside and therefore would be a candidate for a cavity mold. But these suggestions are really departure points upon which many variations can be imposed. For the home shop project, the male mold has many advantages. In the first place, it is generally easier to laminate fiberglass "over" a form rather than "in" a form. Secondly, a smooth, fair outside surface can be achieved by sanding and applying a brush-coat of resin or epoxy paint as a final finish. We should point out that the color coat of resin, or so-called gel coat, is not easily handled by the amateur, hence patching, sanding and painting are often more practical for the novice.

Normally, the one problem that the shop craftsman has to watch out for in the case of plug molds is the matter of releasing the parts, because a glass laminate shrinks slightly after it is cured. Most home shop molds do not have a smooth, slick surface, and while wax and parting film may have been properly applied, the uneven surface does contribute to sticking. When using a male plug mold, a bit of draft or angle (two or three degrees) should be designed into the form to aid release. Another approach is to build the mold in such a way that pieces can be knocked out. The angle brackets shown in the accompanying sketch are one example of demountable fasteners. Another logical method is to use light guage brads in the joints. They should be heavy enough to hold the sections true and tight for the molding operation, but should allow the wood pieces to be pried loose after the laminate is hardened.

Cavity molds cause fewer release problems, unless undercuts are involved. Releasing parts from either type of mold generally requires a certain amount of prying and pulling, but because the laminate is quite resilient it will withstand quite a bit of manhandling without damage. A soft-head mallet, used with reserve but firmness, will help. A thin, flat instrument such as a putty knife will be effective in freeing edges.

Molding Materials

These are the materials required for the box project. The necessity of using reinforcing mat, however, is optional, and fiberglass cloth is easier for the amateur to handle.

Polyester resin and curing agent.
Color pigment paste, if desired.
Fiberglass cloth (10-ounce boat cloth).
Paste wax (Johnson's or equivalent).
Parting film (polyvinyl alcohol or equivalent).

Parting film is only available through plastics supply houses. It can be dispensed with in favor of wax alone.

It is unlikely that the inexperienced person can mold a part without some minor flaws or blemishes. Commonly they occur as wrinkles, pits or void spots, and because of this we suggest having on hand a can of polyester putty. This is a highly filled resin compound that is easy to use and will correct a wide range of imperfections. The putty sets up fast and can be sanded to a fine finish.

Preparation Of The Mold

Two basic concepts of mold constructions have been discussed. For refinement of detail it is hoped that the accompanying sketches will be helpful. One important matter is to see that all corners are rounded sufficiently. This makes the lay-up simpler and provides better strength to the box. A half-inch radius is about right for this design. If fillets have to be built up, it can be done with a variety of materials such as Plastic Wood, wood dough or sculptors' wax.

The amount of care taken in finishing the mold depends on how good a surface is required on the molded parts. The glass-resin laminate will faithfully reproduce every small characteristic of the mold.

After sanding and fairing, the wood surface should be sealed, for which paint, shellac or anything of this nature will suffice. Two or three coats of paste wax should then be applied and buffed out. The addition of two coats of parting film (polyvinyl alcohol) will insure a good release system.

Estimating Thickness Build Up

Judgment will have to be exercised in calculating the thickness required for a given part. However, the problem is not too complicated for the simple box shapes under discussion. Four to six layers of cloth will be adequate for such applications as a battery box, drawer or engine pan. In the case of a hatch cover of reasonable size, the top surface will have to be thicker and stiffer to support the usual loads, and it may be necessary to mold in rib stiffeners or sandwich in a pad of plywood.

Layup Procedure

After the mold is prepared and the number of laminations determined, cut a panel of cloth to the size of the part and experiment to see how it will drape over or in the mold. The open weave design of fiberglass boat cloth will allow it to be formed into very complex radii. Nevertheless, there are limitations and the fabric may have to be cut and tailored to fit certain severe shapes. Even though the fabric is cut in a number of places, the strength of the part will not be impaired if overlaps or staggered butt joints are used between layers.

The first step in molding will be to apply a brush coat of resin to the mold. This may be either a colored gel coat or clear resin. A back-up layer of cloth should then be applied. Form the cloth in place with your hands, perhaps assisted by brush and rubber squeegee. When this layer is firmly in place and all air entrapment removed, it should be allowed to cure. If a compounded color gel coat is to be used, it should be allowed to cure for 30 minutes or so before applying the back-up layer of cloth. This will

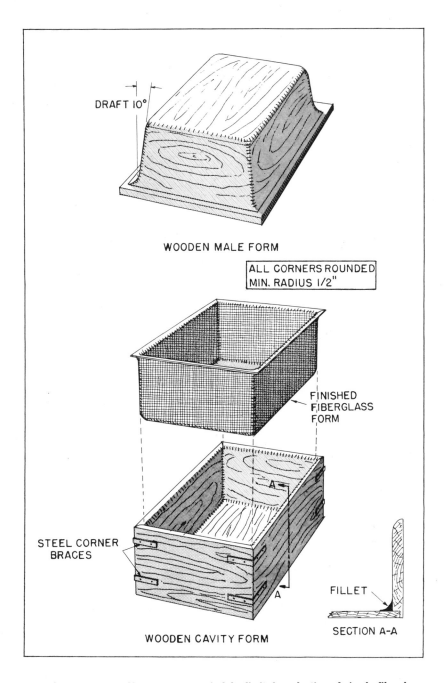

DRAFT 10°

WOODEN MALE FORM

ALL CORNERS ROUNDED
MIN. RADIUS 1/2"

FINISHED
FIBERGLASS
FORM

STEEL CORNER
BRACES

FILLET

WOODEN CAVITY FORM

SECTION A-A

Wooden forms or molds are most practical for limited production of simple fiberglass forms. Basic forms are the plug or male form and the cavity type.

insure a solid color coat of resin without the imprint of the cloth showing through. Additional layers of cloth can now be applied at will. Several layers can be applied at one time if they can be handled.

When the final thickness is arrived at and the surface hardened, it should be sanded smooth. Painting is, of course, optional. Epoxy type paints are suggested since they adhere well to fiberglass and have a hard, smooth finish.

REFERENCES

GENERAL TECHNICAL MANUALS

"Glass Reinforced Plastics," Phillip Morgan, Philosophical Library, Inc., 15 E. 40th St., New York 16, N.Y. $15.

Discussion ranges from the basics of glass and resin formulation to fabrication techniques and adequate treatment of suitable end use applications. Certain chapters need technical background to be fully understood, but much of the book can be absorbed by the individual with mechanical aptitude. Of special note to the boatbuilder is a chapter devoted to boat hull construction written by P.D. Lazlo, founder of the Halmatic Co. in Portsmouth, England.

"Reinforced Plastics—Theory and Practice," M. W. Gaylord, Koppers Company, Inc., Koppers Building, Pittsburgh, Pa. 15219 ($4.95)

A concise and uncomplicated text on glass reinforced plastics. A valuable, quick-reference manual which gives simple answers to common questions related to basic materials and processes.

A SHOP MANUAL FOR GLASS REINFORCED PLASTICS

"Fiber Glass Projects and Procedures," Gerald L. Steele, McKnight & McKnight Publishing Co., Bloomington, Ill. ($4.00).

For general shop projects and procedures, this book is the answer. As far as we know, it is the only one of its kind now available. Mr. Steele is an industrial arts instructor at a Minnesota public school. Fiberglass materials are an excellent new medium for trade schools and general manual training. Mr. Steele has recognized this fact and made a simple, practical presentation on fiberglass-plastic.

MARINE DESIGN AND CONSTRUCTION MANUALS

"Fiberglass Boat Design and Construction," Robert J. Scott, John de Graff, Inc., 34 Oak Avenue, Tuckahoe, N.Y. 10707 (about $10.00)

The latest and most authoritative naval architectural manual on fiberglass boats. A very complete text written by an experienced Gibbs & Cox engineer who has been associated with major fiberglass yacht and commercial hull developments.

"Marine Design Manual For Fiberglass Reinforced Plastics," Gibbs & Cox, Inc., McGraw Hill Book Co., 1221 Avenue of Americas, New York 19, N.Y. (about $15).

This is a formal text on fiberglass boat design developed by the noted Gibbs & Cox marine engineering firm. A number of the chapters are highly technical. For instance, those dealing with calculation of stresses will be beyond the grasp of anyone without an engineering background. However, sections dealing with design criteria and design details are clearly and simply stated, with good accompanying illustrations. Of special interest to the boatbuilder are design examples covering different typical types of pleasure craft.

"Marine Survey Manual for Fiberglass Reinforced Plastics," Gibbs & Co., Inc., available through Owens-Corning Fiberglas Co., 717 Fifth Ave., N.Y. 22, N.Y. ($5.00).

Published in July, 1962, this manual is a sequel to the above mentioned "Design Manual" by the same authors.

The purpose of the book is to provide guidance for the inspection and evaluation of fiberglass boats. It discusses many aspects of fiberglass boat design, fabrication and repair of vital interest to owners, designers and yacht surveyors.

"Provisional Rules For Construction of Fiberglass Yachts," Lloyd's Register of Shipping, 71 Fenchurch St., London EC-3, England (about $10).

In this publication, Lloyd's has come forth with scantling recommendations for fiberglass auxiliaries and power cruisers. While most of the data is based primarily on the Halmatic "hat frame" technique of construction, the whole analysis and approach will be a valuable departure point for any interested naval architect or marine engineer.

"Guide for the Selection of Fiberglass Reinforced Plastics for Marine Structures." Available from: The Society of Naval Architects and Marine Engineers, 74 Trinity Place, New York 6, N.Y.

This publication will be useful for the naval architect, marine engineer or the serious boatman who is technically inclined. The contents include these subjects: basic materials and processes, a classification of laminates, factors influencing their properties. The technical bibliography is considered to be quite comprehensive.

"Fiberglass Boats," Huge DuPlessis. Adlard Coles, available through John de Graff Inc., 34 Oak Avenue, Tuckahoe, New York ($12.50).

The author's talents as a naval architect and plastics engineer combine to produce a highly useful manual.

The book covers fitting out, maintenance, repair and much more. It should be a very worthwhile reference for naval architects, production shops and the serious owners interested in modification and attachments.

The book is profusely illustrated with excellent drawings. A special emphasis has been placed on the wrong and right way of treating design details, an approach which will give the reader a depth of understanding about glass reinforced plastics.